Of Animals and Men

Of Animals and Men

A comparison of human and animal behavior

by
William Bixby

DAVID McKAY CO., INC.
NEW YORK
1968

OF ANIMALS AND MEN

COPYRIGHT © 1968 BY
WILLIAM BIXBY

LIBRARY OF CONGRESS CATALOG CARD NUMBER: 68-30886
MANUFACTURED IN THE UNITED STATES OF AMERICA

Contents

Of Animals and Men

CHAPTER I

Why Aren't All the Tigers Dead?

AT ONE TIME or another everyone has seen the jungles of Africa and Asia. It may have been in a movie, a TV special or an old (or new) chapter of the unending Tarzan series. The scene goes something like this:

The camera scans a great sweep of jungle underbrush—and to make sure we know we are looking at jungle there is often the sound of drums throbbing in a primitive jungle rhythm. An elephant or two may appear beside a water hole and then a tiger is picked up by the camera. This deadly animal is shown skulking along in the undergrowth and stopping once in awhile to show its teeth. The tiger snarls and its ears flatten against its head. It moves on and then stops and snarls again.

The cause of this snarling, it turns out, is another tiger, proceeding through the jungle in the opposite direction—equally frightening and fierce.

Then the two tigers meet in a small clearing and stare at each other for a long moment, tails whipping back and forth and sounds of anger coming from the great tawny throats.

To no one's astonishment, the tigers then leap at one another and fight for their lives in a tangle of toothy mouths, lashing tails and raking claws.

When at last the fight is over, the camera shows the victor slinking off through the jungle and the vanquished lying stretched out dead in the silent clearing.

Very few people mourn the dead tiger in the clearing, and there are many reasons for this. First among them is the feeling that the two savage animals are dangerous and it would be a good thing if both of them were lying dead in the clearing. Second is the feeling that after all they knew what they were getting into and neither one should complain about the powerful law of the jungle and the equally powerful law about the survival of the fittest. (Not many people know just what those laws are, but they are there just the same and have to be obeyed.) Third is the general feeling of excitement that came from watching the fight—and the death of one dangerous beast is not too great a price to pay for that sport. For, after all, the jungle is a very uncivilized place and anything that happens there is simply a good illustration of the fact that men have risen above the savage and dangerous level of jungle beasts.

There used to be a saying about Indians: "The only good Indian is a dead Indian," and the same might be said about tigers. At least a dead tiger cannot hurt you.

Of course it is interesting to go to a zoo and see live tigers in their cages or grottoes—and elephants and lions and all manner of strange beasts. But except for the amusement they give, what good are they anyway?

They, tigers in particular, give hunters an opportunity to prove their bravery. And when a tiger is shot and its head mounted on the wall of the study—mouth open in an eternal snarl of savagery—the general feeling is: Good, there's one less tiger to worry about.

So no one mourns the dead tiger lying in the clearing, killed by a larger, stronger member of the same species.

But the question may rise in someone's mind as he watches the fatal scene described above. Why, that person might ask, aren't all the tigers dead?

To arrive at an answer after asking this question requires a long journey—a trip you might say—that is painful to a lot of people, impossible for some, but a great adventure for those who manage it.

The journey is not long or hard because of the distance traveled. It is hard because it often makes a fool of you as you go along. And no one likes that, least of all scientists and other people in respectable professions.

The person who asked the question: Why aren't all the tigers dead, if they go around killing one another? may not have been a genius but he was bright enough to see what was going on right under his eyes and think about what occurred—or seemed to occur.

The people who watched the TV or movie screen and believed what they saw were not necessarily stupid. They had just been brainwashed. For what the movie producer did was to show the people what they believed would happen anyway. In a very brief way, here is what viewers believed: Animals like tigers are lower forms of life. By lower form of life we mean lower than man, who is highest. Lower forms of life do not understand the value of life. These lower forms of life often live in the jungle, just as we have seen on the screen. They are savage and uncivilized. They go around killing one another.

So, the producer showed them a scene in which one tiger killed another.

But what about the person who asked the crazy question: Why aren't all the tigers dead?

He said something like this to himself: If there is a country in which 1000 tigers live and they each try to kill a tiger a day—and succeed—then in one day there would be 500 dead tigers. The next day there would be 250 dead tigers, with only 250 left. On the third day there would be 125 tigers left. On the fourth day (and here is where it gets tricky) there would either be 62 healthy tigers and one very sick one (half alive so to say) or 63 healthy tigers (one tiger failed to get his quota)—and so on.

Very shortly, as anyone can plainly see, there would be only one tiger left. He would be the strongest and healthiest tiger in the land—the only one. And that tiger could do anything he wanted except reproduce himself (or herself). Then when old age came, the graying tiger would crawl into a cave and die. And there would be no more tigers.

As a small boy, the person who asked the above question had read many stories of cavemen and prehistoric life and he had seen pictures of little men with big clubs wrapped in animal skins huddled around a fire while a giant saber-toothed tiger snarled at them from out of the jungle. From these scenes he had gotten the idea that tigers had been around a long time. Evidently the two ideas—that tigers have been around a long time and that they go around killing one another—can't both be true.

To check on his boyhood memories the observant person hurried to a natural history museum and sure enough there were skeletons of tigers whose bones had creaked around in the jungles thousands of years ago—so it was true that tigers have been around for a long time.Then the other idea cannot be true.

In other words tigers do not go around killing each other.

Tigers have sharp teeth and they use them to bite. They have outrageous fingernails and can scratch right through a great many objects. They are fierce and they fight one another many times. How is it, then, that they manage to keep from killing each other?

Such animals as tigers are called carnivores. They are hunters and they daily, or nightly, need meat for food. This they get by using their teeth and claws to catch and kill smaller animals for snacks and feasts.

There is nothing unnatural in this although it upsets the more sheltered viewers of the world scene. There are many predators on the face of the earth who go about killing other animals for food. Man among them. Dr. Louis Leakey's recent finds in the Olduvai Gorge in Africa indicate that the earliest man-like creature yet uncovered, *Homo habilis,* was a hunter and ate meat that he killed.

All carnivores like tigers and wolves and lions have the suitable armament to keep them alive: claws, teeth, and the

5

short tempers to use them. These are deadly weapons. On many occasions these animals fight among themselves (for very good reasons which will be revealed later) but they always stop short of killing one another.

What stops them? They have read few books and attended fewer universities where the idea of live and let live is taught. How, then, do they know that they are doing something wrong if they carve each other up too seriously?

To discover an answer to this question, scientists of animal behavior, many of whom are now called ethologists, have spent years in the only laboratory that they have: the world of the natural animals themselves. There, hidden in blinds, perched on platforms in trees or floating on the surface of the sea, they have observed the behavior of the animals. And only now, in the latter part of the twentieth century, are answers coming that promise to change many theories and many sciences that have to do with mankind.

In some ways it is as if the result of all the observation is telling man that he himself has been blind for centuries about the "lower" animals and about his own nature.

One of the results of ethological observation, is the fact that animals are always fighting among themselves. Monkeys scream at other monkeys; certain fishes rush about under water quarreling; beatles battle; and tigers snarl and roll around in the underbrush.

But only in rare cases does one member of a species kill another of the same species.

In the jungle, at the right time of day, a man with a tape recorder could get a wonderful sound record of the uproar

6

going on. He would have the high-pitched screams of birds calling threateningly back and forth, the chatter of monkeys insulting one another and various squeals, grunts and groans of what seem to be fights to the finish in the bush. The why of all this fighting must wait for another chapter, but the thing that stops these animals from killing can be found in all the hubbub that goes on.

Gorillas, for example, are regarded by uninformed people as ferocious and deadly beasts. And they have been observed in their natural settings on the verge of a fight many times. Two male gorillas will approach one another with many threatening gestures. They will face each other and utter loud roars. The hair on their bodies will rise and make each one look bigger than he really is. One will beat on his chest with his paws (or hands, if you like) and the other will thump himself mightily, too. They will bare their teeth and roar again and again. At this point most humans would leave the scene in terror. And in many cases, one of the gorillas does just that. He has been out-terrified by the other gorilla and the fight is over.

These threatening gestures are common among animals who seem about to start an all out fight. Anyone who has observed a cat on the verge of a fight (or one that is frightened and thinks it is being attacked) knows how its fur stands up, the tail increases enormously in size and what was a small cat becomes a larger, menacing creature. The yowls the cat makes are, at night, enough to make the hair of your own head or neck stand up, too.

Here then is one clue to the safety valves in fighting among animals: they sometimes out-threaten one another and thus avoid actual conflict—where teeth, claws, hooves or horns are actually used.

As ethologists gathered their laboratory data in the wild another and more important safety valve against murder came to their attention: ceremonial fighting or what has been called ritualized combat.

A typical example of this behavior and its observation comes from a report by Fritz Walther, a scientist in a German animal research project. He was studying the fighting behavior of a normally timid animal—the oryx antelope found in Africa. The males of this species of antelope have long, nearly straight and extremely sharp horns—deadly weapons indeed. If one male wanted to kill another who was unaware of the attack, death or at least serious injury would result. All the attacking male would have to do is wait until his enemy was feeding with his head down, run at him with his own head lowered and drive his sharp horns into the exposed flank and belly of the other. The horns would penetrate easily and the attacked antelope would be killed.

But how do they actually fight?

Fritz Walther watched and saw that the two bulls approached each other, strutting and heads held high. They walked stifflegged and stopped only when they were "alongside" one another, flank opposite flank. Each still had a good view of his opponent because the animal's eyes, like those of many other animals, are in the sides of their head. He can see as easily sideward as forward.

The animals turned, then, facing each other as though on

some agreed upon signal. One moved in and lowered his head, swinging the long horns and striking those of his opponent. The struck animal endured the blow and then it was his turn. He swung and the other animal took the shock of the horns. There was no stabbing motion; rather a slashing attack aimed at the other's horns. Walther saw immediately that this was almost identical to two men with swords slashing, not at one another at the moment, but at each one's sword.

After a period of "fencing" as he called it, the two bull antelopes locked their horns and placed their foreheads together and began a pushing match with twisting motions of the locked horns, placing great strain on their necks. This pushing and neck wrestling went on until one of the antelopes admitted defeat and pulled back his head. He turned and walked away and the other antelope simply stood still, triumphant in victory but without having killed his enemy.

During the struggle, Walther observed another astonishing thing. After one particularly violent bit of neck-twisting, one of the antelopes lost contact with the other and was turned completely around so that his flank and tail end were exposed to his enemy. Now, if ever, was the time for a deadly blow at the unprotected and vulnerable rear. But the antelope with the advantage made no move to kill his enemy. He waited until the other animal had turned and was again ready to lock horns in the ceremonial, the ritual fight.

This method of fighting among animals has its strict rules. It also has a strict order of performance. The first part of the fight, like that of the terrifying gorilla, is display. In this act, the animal, whatever he is, makes himself as threatening and terrifying as possible. If he is a fighting tropical fish, he swells up, extends his fins as far out as possible and his colors, if he has bright colors, actually become brighter and more colorful as he prepares to fight. The gorilla makes himself as large as possible by spreading his arms, rolling his shoulders forward so they extend a maximum distance from his neck and the hair rises. (In place of going to the jungle and watching gorillas do this, all you have to do is watch a "professional" wrestling match on television. Here all the gorilla motions are carefully used to terrify, not the opponent in this case, but the audience. You may practice the same thing if you like. Let your arms hang loose. Then twist your hands inward toward your body. This thrusts out your elbows and moves your shoulders outward. You look bigger that way. The villain in the TV match frequently does this so that the audience will first fear him and then hate him—which is what he is getting paid for.) Nearly all fighting animals do something like this.

Dogs bristle, growl, bare their teeth and stand side-to-side to show how big they are. Cats bristle hugely and hiss and yowl—and also stand side-to-side. Birds' feathers rise and ruffle up, making them larger, beaks clack and some birds, like geese, hiss alarmingly. Birds also often spread and flap their wings and, if they have crests or other display plumage, it rises or fans out and the animal looks much bigger than it actually is.

All of these display and threat gestures are part of Act I of the quarrel. And many times, as has been mentioned, it is enough to win the fight. Hence no one is killed.

Act II of the ceremonial fight is a series of steps, fully understood by both fighters, like the oryx antelope fight described above. Among most horned animals like mountain sheep, deer, and wild goats, the deadly horns are all used to lock foreheads together and allow the pushing and neck twisting contest to go on. (Deer hunters in the wilderness of Canada or the northern United States have come across skeletons of two bucks, their complex horns locked so tightly that they could not release one another and the two animals died of starvation.)

In many ways these ritual fights are tests of strength for the selection of mates—or the winning of approval of the female—in the ancient evolutionary patterns of selection. In the case of one species of lizard, observed by a Viennese scientist, the lizards went through the display part of the fight and then one lizard grabbed the other's neck in his mouth. The other one waited without moving. Finally the first lizard loosened his grip and then the positions were reversed. The bitten lizard bit the other one's neck. But there was no wound inflicted. It was an alternate contest between the two lizards of jaw strength against neck muscle strength. After trading bites, the lizard that lost turned around and ran off. And the scientist observed that it was not always the most bitten lizard that ran. If an attacking lizard found he'd got hold of a lizard with a stronger neck—too strong to be impressed by his bite—he would be the one who broke off the fight and ran.

One of the most interesting ritual fights in the world occurs among members of various species of fish—particularly the brightly colored varieties.

Two fish, strangers but of the same species, approach in the water and suddenly see one another. They are instantly torn between two desires: to flee and to fight. The desire to flee makes them turn aside from one another while the desire to fight makes them display their brightest (and presumably most terrifying colors). Fear makes their fins rise until they are as large as they can ever appear to be.

Motionless in the water in the grip of two oppositely directed impulses the fish seem momentarily hypnotized. One of them swings his tail toward the other, but his position does not change. Although you cannot see it, he has just struck his opponent. When he moved his tail he set up a small swirling stream of water that rushed over and hit the body of the other fish. The fish who got hit takes the blow and, in his tiny fish brain, decides whether or not he ought to go on with the fight. If he thinks he should, he flicks his tail and sends a tailstream to hit the first fish. This method of trading blows (like the lizards alternately biting each other's neck) can go on for some time. If the contest isn't decided by the tailstreams, the two fish face each other and approach until they can each grab the jaw of the other. In this way, mouth-to-mouth, they push and tug at one another until one of them admits defeat and lets go, swimming rapidly away.

Long observation of certain fishes has shown the interesting fact that only fishes who are very evenly matched in size and strength ever get to the mouth-to-mouth phase.

If a large fish comes upon a smaller fish, the small one, being nobody's fool, lets the run-away impulse take over. He tucks his fins down, turns off his colors and makes himself scarce. If a medium-size fish comes upon a large one, he may fool himself a bit and think he can win the fight. But with the first thump of the tailstream of water against his side, he quickly changes his mind, hauls down his fins and leaves. In other words, only two fish who are very evenly matched get to the mouth-tugging stage, the actual fight. And then they can go at it on even terms until one of them is exhausted and gives up. And all the ritual fighting *is* exhausting. Antelopes with forehead-to-forehead pushing push until they are tired. It is not a play contest. Like Indian hand wrestling, it is a test of strength, with strict rules that are always observed. If the fish, for example, wanted to cheat, they easily could because when they are trying to kill they do not grasp jaws and wrestle. Many species, for example, use their noses as a battering ram and try to strike their prey (or a larger fish that wants to eat them) a ramming blow with their noses in an unguarded flank. If one of the ritual-fighting fish was allowed to cheat by his control mechanism, he could take advantage of the other when they are broadside to each other with their heads turned away. The cheater could turn head on to the other's flank and ram him. He never does this unless he is engaged in a serious non-ritual fight and he must be driven to it by extreme circumstances.

This inability to cheat holds for other animals as well. Antlered deer, for example, fight much as the oryx antelope does.

They walk first parallel to each other with a great display of antlers and high-stepping hooves looking for all the world like two drum majors trying to out-prance one another. Then, at a signal only both of them understand, they turn to face each other, lock horns and begin head-wrestling. An observer of this ritual fight noticed a slight slip-up in the routine one time. One of the deer thought the signal had been given and he turned to face his opponent. But the other one strutted proudly on—bringing his exposed and vulnerable flank directly opposite the antlers of the deer that had turned. Here was a golden opportunity to deliver an injurious blow—one that would have ended the fight then and there. But the deer that had turned was not permitted to cheat. With a slight air of confusion, he, too, turned back and caught up with his rival, prancing along-side him and waiting for the signal to tell him (correctly this time) when to turn and lock horns.

So the ritual fight among such animals serves to exhaust them and satisfy the urge to fight without harming the species at all.

But what of animals that have deadly weapons like long sharp teeth and claws or animals accustomed to killing for their food? How can these creatures carry on a ritual fight and not kill each other?

Scientists now realize that in the long, long, course of evolution, patterns of behavior have been developed in every species. Each species, in other words, has patterns that control actions built into their genes that help them prevail—exactly as a pro-grammed computer is ready to respond on the right signal. Such programmed patterns are rightly called instincts as they do not, of course, require a high degree of intelligence in the individual animals—any more than a computer which is only metal and circuits could be called highly intelligent. But in animals, sight, sounds, smells, touches, and tastes all bring forth the required action at the right time. The "how" of that programming is still largely a mystery to man.

In predators like wolves, for example, the teeth are the principal weapon. If two wolves approach each other with threatening gestures, a fight may take place (unless one manages to out-threaten the other). In wolves, as in most dogs, the aim of a serious fight is to sink the teeth into the neck of the other and bite through the artery running near the surface on that part of the body. If this were done, death probably would result.

Careful study of the fight behavior of wolves has shown that after the snarling and snapping have started, the one who feels he is getting the worst of the fight can stop the other's attack instantly by making what scientists have come to call an appeasing or submissive gesture. In the wolf, this is done by turning the teeth away from the opponent and baring the unprotected neck. The wolf is saying, in effect, "I give up. Don't kill me."

The key to the motion that stops the winning fighter from killing his opponent is the hiding of his own weapons—his teeth. But in doing this, he exposes his throat. The reaction of the winner is immediate. There is not just a "slowing down" of the fight. Even though the winning wolf is in mid-lunge at the beaten wolf when the gesture of appeasement is made, the winner does not bite.

This sudden stoppage of the wolf's aggression can, according to Konrad Lorenz, one of the world's leading ethologists, be due only to the triggering of an inhibition, a powerful inner force that is, in the case of the wolf, instinctual.

A similarly powerful inner force that stops aggressive behavior in wolves (as well as domesticated dogs) is the sight of puppy behavior. For many years observers wondered what kept adult wolves from fighting seriously with the young in a pack —even their own young. A six or eight month-old wolf, for example, is nearly as large as an adult and has all the same color markings by that time. But the immature wolf would be no match for a seasoned adult in a fight. They never fight, however, because the immature wolf, when threatened or when approaching a strange adult wolf will go through many of the behavior motions we associate with puppies. They will try to lick the adult and nuzzle it. They will crouch down and in many cases will roll over on their backs—exposing their defenseless bellies. This behavior stops the attacking wolf from doing serious damage to the younger member of the pack.

So there are several types of behavior, several motions that trigger the inhibition in wolves and other predators with dangerous weapons against killing their own kind. What each of these various motions has in common is the element of submission or appeasement: the admission of defeat or, if you will, the admission that the opponent is superior.

Observers who have actually witnessed a pair of tigers or lions fighting in the jungle have been astonished by one strange fact: when the fight is over, after all the roaring and threatening and after a lightning-like tussle is over, in and around the underbrush, the fighting animals part and there are no quantities of spilled blood, there are no gaping wounds and above all, no dead tiger stretched out in the camera's view.

For even though the actual fight proceeded too fast for the observer to record every bit of the ritual fight, the ritual fight was in fact what he observed.

And that is why all the tigers are not dead.

Men, of course, not being tigers—or any kind of "lower" animal—do go around killing members of their own species. During World War II, throughout our world, we killed 51,000,000 people. A record.

CHAPTER II

What Is Home to a Dog?

THERE ARE VERY few dogs running around loose these days. In the suburbs of cities, where houses are placed on small rectangular lots, and gardens grow, there are even fewer dogs on the loose. The good ladies of the land have found that dogs sometimes dig in the dirt enthusiastically and uproot flower beds. So the licensing and leashing laws have been passed and it is difficult to find a loose dog who can show you in no time at all what his home is.

Occasionally you come across an unleashed dog or two, however. If you walk along a suburban sidewalk in front of the neat square lawns you may see one sitting on the porch just waiting for someone like you to bark at. (It's pretty boring being a suburban dog and they don't want to miss the action any more than you do.) Let's say you walk in a strange neighborhood and find such a dog. It may be a small dog or a large one but when he sees you coming, his ears go up and he watches you with complete concentration as you approach. He doesn't know you and you don't know him. You decide to ignore the dog, be completely neutral. But he does not ignore you. As you near the corner of the lot on which the dog is located, he rushes toward you with hair bristling and a torrent of ferocious barks coming from his open, tooth-filled mouth.

If the dog is large, the hair on the back of your neck will probably rise and your skin will prickle with fear. You walk along trying to look as if nothing were going on. In a furious rush, the dog reaches the corner of the lot, just as you arrive there. He brakes to a halt and the barking continues. Growls, threats, tooth-waving and loud, unnerving barks follow you as you proceed along the sidewalk. The dog backs off a few steps and rushes again—but always halts right at the edge of the sidewalk. He follows you along until you reach the far corner of the lot and right there, if you proceed on your way, the dog leaves you. He doesn't come out on the sidewalk after you. It is as if an invisible leash or rope held the dog within the boundaries of the lot. The barking goes on and on but the hair on your neck settles down. You remember the saying, a barking dog never bites—and besides he hasn't followed you.

After awhile quiet once more settles on the neighborhood. At the end of the block you glance back and the dog has returned to the porch, where he sits waiting for more excitement. And then out of the corner of your eye, you see a large dog actually running loose, skulking through hedges and loping across lots stopping from time to time to sniff at bushes and trees. His head is down as he travels and since he is not going in a direction that will bother you, you don't feel frightened. But the loping dog is going in a direction that takes him across the lot with the house and the porch with the dog on it. The loping dog starts across the green square of lawn and suddenly the dog on the porch sees the other dog. Outraged barks ring out again. The dog leaps from the porch and rushes at the other dog. Here, you say, is the start of a ferocious dog fight. The loping dog is even larger than the porch-sitting dog and it would appear that the larger dog should get the better of the smaller one.

The smaller dog does not seem worried about size at all. He roars toward the other dog and, wonder of wonders, the larger dog turns tail and runs without a single show of tooth or answering bark. The porch-sitter chases the larger dog away but he goes only to the edge of the little square of lawn that marks the edge of the lot—or a few steps further. Then he stops and hurls more barks into the air after the fleeing animal.

Home, to the porch-sitting dog, is quite obviously the square of grass, the lot and the house. It is his home, his territory.

The word territory today is used a lot by ethologists and a great deal of recent study has gone into what "territory" really is, what good it does an animal to have a territory and how the idea of territory can mean so many different things to so many different animals.

The idea of territory goes a long way back among observers of nature and animals, back more than two thousand years where scholars have dug up remarks about territory in the writings of Aristotle and, later, the great Roman naturalist, Pliny. These ancient gentlemen remarked on the fact that eagles seemed to have need of a certain amount of land to find food for themselves and they observed that if other eagles came on the scene, a couple would fight them off. But these remarks were taken by those who read Aristotle and Pliny to be only interesting, not very important.

It remained for a modern pioneer naturalist to direct scientific attention to the entire idea of an animal's territory and, more importantly, to what territory was all about. The man's name was Eliot Howard.

Nowhere in science is there a stranger picture of a scientist than Eliot Howard. He was not, by profession, a scientist. He was an amateur. But all his days he studied birdlife in England near his home at Hartlebury. Long before dawn, each morning of his adult life he would get up, put on heavy clothing against the chill weather and take his binoculars and disappear in the mists over meadows and through woodland and heather. By breakfast time, when the rest of his family was up, he would be back. After eating he would turn into a businessman. He would put on his executive suit, get into his car and drive to the train station. Through the day he served as a director of a large English steel company. Then he would go home like any commuting businessman, have dinner with his family and go to bed early. There was one more thing. After dinner and before going to bed he would often sit for an hour or two at a time silently smoking his pipe and thinking.

Several books came out of his thinking and the most important was a modest little volume titled *Territory in Bird Life*. It was published in 1920. At first this book attracted little notice but as the years went on other scientists began to pay attention to it.

During the morning observations around his home and throughout England, Eliot Howard made notes on all that he observed and asked himself questions, questions that some observed bird behavior had raised in his mind. Why, for example, did the male bird leave the female birds just as the breeding season was coming on? It didn't make sense. Whole flocks of buntings and sparrows would feed together for the winter season and it seemed that in these large flocks there would be plenty of chance for a male and female bird to pair off and begin building a nest. But that is not what happened. As spring came on, the males would fly to the traditional breeding grounds, they would not flock as before.

Instead they each chose a bush or patch of heather and chased away any bird of their species that came near. Each male bird would stake out a territory for himself. It became clear, too, that all chirping and singing had nothing to do with the glories of spring. The singing birds were warning each other not to intrude on the singer's territory. If some male bird did intrude, the owner of the territory would promptly chase him away.

Soon the female birds began to arrive on the breeding grounds—those areas where nesting and the raising of the young annually took place. As May gave way to June, the birds paired off. Sometimes quite rapidly and at other times slowly. Some male birds defended their territory for weeks before a female stopped to inspect the area and remained with the male.

Then the question: what is the territory for? occurred to Howard in his long evening's think period. His theory, which is still regarded as true for many species, was that to bring the next generation of birds safely into the world, there had to be more to it than merely producing eggs and hatching them. For the young birds are born helpless and must be fed for a period of time before they can shift for themselves. This meant that there had to be food nearby for the birds to gather quickly to feed three or four hungry mouths. So, before the nest was built, even before pairing between birds had happened, the problem of the food supply was solved by the male bird. He made sure of it by defining a territory that he could defend and he chose a place that had a food supply.

Since Howard's time the whole idea of territory has been examined carefully by hundreds of researchers. They have found that many species of birds and animals possess what can only be called a "territorial instinct." Some animals will stake out a territory and hold it for life. Others will defend a territory only during the breeding season. Even fish of certain species stake out a territory. Of course its boundaries are not visible to human eyes, but the fish know where the boundaries are and defend them just as if they were as clearly marked as the boundary between the grass lawn of the dog's small plot and the concrete sidewalk.

Territories vary greatly in size from species to species and seem to be determined by the geography of the place as well as the needs of the animals. Certain sea birds, for example, can be observed nesting in very close quarters. A crowded shelf of rock on a cliff overlooking the sea was examined by Howard. On it were hundreds of nesting Guillemots—a small form of auk. Howard quite naturally wondered why some birds needed a lot of space for their territory like the buntings while others needed only a few square feet for their nests.

His reasoning was that the birds need narrow rock shelves on cliffs for nesting and that there were other requirements of the site that were not immediately clear to an observer. The sea, for example, must come close to the base of the cliff and not be too shallow (or absent on a low tide). The rock cliff face should be nearly vertical with no great projections between the nesting site and the water. These odd requirements, he reasoned, came from the fact of Guillemot life that when the young bird is ready to leave the nest it is not yet able to fly. The best it can do is stagger down through the air like a crippled glider and plop into the water where the food is. From there on it is on its own. It soon experiments with flying until it is strong enough to take off and land whenever or wherever it chooses. Naturally if the cliff had projections or if there were boulders sticking up out of the water below, the danger to the young Guillemot in its first frantic glide to the sea could easily end in death.

Since this is not helpful in survival of the species, the Guillemot seeks a rocky shelf for nesting that will give the young flier the best chance for a start in life.

Such perfect sites are few and far between. When located, a number of Guillemots must share them. Unlike the bunting, the seabird has a very minor food problem. At the base of the cliff in the surging water is all the food he needs. The female can take a short flight from the nest and return in a few moments. So the space required for buntings is not required for Guillemots. Hence they nest close together and arrange their nests so the space between them is not less than two neck lengths. Adjacent pairs stay out of pecking distance of one another.

Today, the value of the territorial instinct is obvious. It was not obvious during the time that Howard made his quiet but extremely important report on bird territorial behavior. Ethologists now accept the idea that the most important value of territorial behavior for any species lies in assuring a food supply. Territory holding, in fact, acts not only to preserve the species, but also to control its members' reproduction. For if a male bird does not find and hold a territory, no female bird will pair with him.

There are cases—among gulls, among seals and among members of the antelope family—where not all eligible males find a mate. In these cases, young males who cannot locate a site on the breeding ground form a bachelor group that is ignored by the females. If a bachelor bull seal, for example, wants to attract a female he does not approach her. He charges onto the territory of an older stronger bull and fights him for possession of the ground. If he wins, he gets the females (for bull seals have harems of females). If he loses, he goes back to the bachelor pool and does more pushups until he feels strong enough to challenge a territory-owning bull again. Gulls, too, have their bachelor groups. In fact it is so much a part of gull social life that a part of the breeding ground is set apart for the young male gulls. They squabble and fight, growing stronger. Perhaps not this season, but the next, one or more of them will be strong enough to invade an older gull's territory.

The question: what defines a territory? has nearly as many answers as there are territorial animals who seek and hold territory. Among the birds that Eliot Howard studied in England was the moor hen. This bird makes its nests along the shores of a pond among the rushes. For food, it scours the waters of the pond and a number of moor hens might share the same water for food gathering until the breeding season approaches. Then, as Howard observed, a change comes over the pond. The once peaceful moor hens become quarrelsome. Squabbles break out. Gradually the group of moor hens breaks up. The pairs swim only in separate parts of the pool. At night, each pair retreats to a particular part of the marshy shore. Within a short time each pair has established itself as "owners" of a portion of shore and a portion of lake surface. The stronger pairs have larger territories. But just how each pair keeps track of its share of water surface, no observer yet has discovered.

Most bird species and some animals take and hold territory only just before and during the breeding season. But there are animals that hold a territory all of their lives. Some live in that territory as pairs, raising young each season and then forcing the adolescents out into the world on their own. Other animals form large families that stay together for several seasons and still others produce an entire tribe of animals where inter-breeding can take place and the territory is defended by all members of the tribe.

One of the original and now classic studies of animal be-havior that involved territory was that of C. R. Carpenter titled *Behavior and Social Relations of the Gibbon.*

The gibbon is considered to be one of the "higher primates" which includes the anthropoid apes and man. He is, however, just barely in that classification and may be thought of as exist-ing between the monkeys and the apes, from an evolutionary point of view. The social status of being lower than the apes but higher than monkeys does not bother the gibbon at all. He happily brachiates among the jungle foliage of Thailand and is in fact probably the world's best brachiator. Tarzan tried this but was never as successful as the gibbon. In brachiating, the gibbon swings through trees by holding onto limbs above him with his tremendously long arms. At times he seems to be flying, so rapid is his movement through the jungle.

In studying the gibbon, the scientists in Dr. Carpenter's party watched the activities of twenty-one different groups whose size ran from a single pair with no baby gibbons to a family group that had three generations of offspring—totalling six members. Each group had a territory in the jungle and the surrounding groups kept them inside their territory. There was a favorite sleeping place for each group in vine-covered trees. There was a water supply nearby in each territory and there were food supplies in trees or in bamboo clumps and fruit vines. The groups did not often travel very far. When they did, they sometimes got into a neighbor's territory. The neighbors would start calling out warnings and the group that had trespassed would call among themselves and soon retreat to their home grounds. Dr. Carpenter did not observe any actual fighting among the gibbons although he assumed there was a scrap from time to time. In all the cases he observed, warning calls were enough to discourage an invading group.

Of course the larger groups had larger territories. The small groups had as little as thirty acres to wander in without going off their territory while the larger groups staked out as much as 100 acres.

The search for food was the greatest cause of trespassing among the gibbon society. If figs ripened on several trees near the edge of one group's territory, the odor would attract a neighboring group and they would try a little shoplifting.

Usually they were caught at it and then the jungle would be filled with various cries of anger and warning and, eventually, the advice to retreat.

Within a territory most animals like the gibbon soon have the space completely organized. As soon as a territory is gained, the group or pair choose some place near the center of the space for sleeping—and they never sleep anywhere else unless they are disturbed. Paths are laid out leading to the food supply or the drinking spot. The animals travel along these paths and rarely stray from them. Sometimes there is a play area for the young. Gibbons, which spend most of their lives above the ground, were seen by Dr. Carpenter to spend most of their time in the middle levels of trees. They did not often go to the tops and only occasionally to the ground. Gibbons can run along the ground, standing up as well as most apes and monkeys but they always stay close to a clump of trees or bushes so they can get off the ground quickly in case of attack by a predator. Their paths through the trees had to be guessed at by Dr. Carpenter since he wasn't able to follow them personally.

Animals that live on the ground give the best evidence of this division of space by the occupying family or tribe. As soon as animals gain a territory they form the habit of paths and particular places for particular needs. Birds, as Howard saw them, always approach their nests from the same direction. It becomes a habit with them and they never break the habit. To test this, Howard at one time cleared away the twigs and branches on one side of a low bush in which a pair of birds had built its nest. The female was accustomed to approaching the nest from the opposite side and Howard watched as she flew toward it with a beakful of food. She saw the cleared space with the nest and her young birds clearly visible as she flew toward the bush. She lighted on a branch directly in front of the cleared space. There were the hungry mouths and the cheeping voices calling for breakfast. All she had to do was move forward through the cleared space a foot or two and she would be home. But her habit had been to come to the nest from the other side—even if this meant hopping all around through the thick branches. As Howard watched she again did just that. She ignored the easy path and went around through the leaves until she reached the point where she always had entered the nest. Then, and only then, did she go to the edge of the nest.

Another example of this planning of the home territory and sticking to the plan was observed when a pair of captured rhinoceroses were put in a zoo. They were given a large fenced enclosure and enclosed sleeping dens which were in fact cages. For the first several days, the rhinos were kept locked up so they would get used to their quarters and not panic on being suddenly let loose. Finally they were allowed into the grassy area outside which was to be their new territory. They both came from their cage-dens cautiously into the great outdoors. The zoo keepers had planned plenty of space for the two animals but, fortunately, had not tried to divide the space for them. Within a day or so, the rhinos had made their own division. Pathways were formed by simply walking along them. The only spot decided upon for them by man was the feeding place. On their own, the rhinos used a part of the space for a play area, another for a resting area where they could nap during the day. At their watering place they had a drinking spot. and a bathing spot. There was also a browsing area in the tall grass, for snacks. The bathroom was established near the gate to the enclosure—the only place from which, they felt, any danger could come. This location of the bathroom "marked" their territory and the odor of their excrement would warn away any possible rhino who might try to intrude.

The habits they established were firm and never broken. They would not leave the paths they had marked out. They never browsed in the play area or played in the browsing area. If called by their keeper who was on one side of the enclosure, they would not cut across the grass but would follow the paths around until they came to him.

This behavior of captured animals has been seen also in wild ones. It is not a result of their being in captivity but is an example of how they behave in their natural homes in all corners of the world.

There seems to be, Dr. Carpenter concluded in his study of the gibbon, a biological need for nearly all animals to have some territory. Many species of animals establish rigid habits within their home areas and never vary from them unless men drive them out or panic them.

The only things that can drive animals from their territories are a lack of food or water and being overpowered by a stronger neighboring pair or tribe. If drought comes to the land and the food and water supplies are no longer available, the animals will try to migrate to new territories. If overpowering neighbors seize the territory they will accept a reduced space or in some cases disappear from the area altogether in their search for another favorable place.

The question: how do animals know the boundaries of their territories? The answer is often beyond man's understanding. In large animals that men have observed there is a definite marking of boundaries. The marking is usually a matter of odor. Many, like rhinos, use the odor of their excrement to mark boundaries and among dogs the commonly observed urination on posts and trees is a marking device.

But there are other animals that have special glands that produce the marking scent. Certain deer have scent glands in their hind hooves. Wild pigs have a gland on their backs that actually squirts the scent marking the boundary. Scientists know now that the singing of birds when they reach the breeding grounds in the spring is a method of marking the boundaries to their territories. But what of fish? How can they mark boundaries in the shifting currents of water beneath the sea? We do not know this—nor do we know how the moor hens stake out claims to their portions of a pond's surface.

An observer floating with a mask above brightly marked tropical fish has watched a specimen who may live in a nook of the coral-strewn shore. When another fish of the same species comes along, the lurking fish turns into a fighting fish and he rushes out to drive the intruder off. He chases the other fish a short way and then turns back. Somehow or other he knows when he has reached the boundary of his territory and he goes no further in pushing the enemy out.

It is curious, too, that all this uproar over territory is directed at members of the defenders' own species. Rhinoceroses in their territory, for example, will defend it only against other rhinoceroses. If a zebra or giraffe wanders onto their territory, the resident rhinoceroses pay no attention to them.

There is no longer any doubt in the scientific world that territory has a great deal to do with the survival of different species of animals—from fish to the higher primates like the gibbon. But as they study the problem, scientists admit that there is no one single and simple thing that possessing a territory does. The whole scheme of nature is so complicated that different scientists have found different things that territory does for an animal.

There is no question but that the selection of territories makes it next to impossible under ordinary conditions for the food supply to be destroyed. It also keeps the population of a species from being destroyed all at once or at all by another species that preys on it. It affects the size of the population and limits breeding. It provides security for the members of a family or tribe. It assures an orderly breeding season with time and space to care for the young. Territory cuts down on the spread of disease that might wipe out the species and prevents parasites from infecting large groups. In the case of species that share a territory as a tribe, it gives all members a strong bond to the group and allows for the orderly living of all its members. In short, the whole mysterious and little understood business of territorial behavior assures as much harmony as possible.

So if you have a dog, and that dog barks whenever anyone

(particularly another dog) comes onto his home territory, don't punish him for it. For even the most domesticated pet dogs still have this territorial instinct. They will find a favorite spot in the house for resting. They will simply take over the house and the lot or lawn as their territory. Why? Because it's their home. That's why.

It is almost impossible for anyone to study animals without asking questions about man's behavior and how it relates to animals. Is it similar in any way, or not? In the case of the ritualized fighting without killing of the tigers—and fish and antelopes—the answer unfortunately is: not very similar. Man doesn't behave that morally.

Man does, however, have an urge to take and hold territory. Great groups of men form nations, smaller ones form provinces or states or villages. In each case there is more than geography that makes it a territory. There has to be a desire to defend the territory against invaders. We have all defended our territories of hometown, state and country, at least verbally, against those who speak badly of them.

Families are the smallest territory-holding unit among men just as among the animals. Families also have border fights with their neighbors at times. House lots are surveyed carefully and trespass is punishable by law. A farm family in the country protects its fields as stubbornly as the suburban homeowner protects his little plot of ground. The farmer, of course, makes his living and grows much of his food on his land while the suburban man does not. But both hold and defend territory.

This territorial instinct has always been part of man's nature. It has been celebrated in song and story and legend and one of the most obvious "stories" about man's territorial instinct is the poem by Robert Frost titled "Mending Wall."

In the poem Frost tells of a yearly springtime chore he shared with his farmer neighbor. They "walk the line" between their territories to mend the stone wall which is the boundary. The winter has toppled stones, some on Frost's side and some on his neighbor's. And each man picks up the stones that have fallen to each and places them back on the wall, building the boundary between them. Half kidding, half in earnest, Frost asks the farmer what the wall is good for since:

"He is all pine and I am apple orchard.
My apple trees will never get across
And eat the cones under his pines, I tell him.
He only says, 'Good fences make good neighbors.'"

Frost worries about it though and remarks that before he built a wall he'd ask

"What I was walling in or walling out,
And to whom I was like to give offense."

But he says this to himself, not aloud to the farmer. Then he concludes the poem by reaching, with words, far back into mankind's beginnings:

"I see him there
Bringing a stone grasped firmly by the top
In each hand, like an old-stone savage armed.

He moves in darkness as it seems to me,
Not of woods only and the shade of trees.
He will not go behind his father's saying,
And he likes having thought of it so well.
He says again, 'Good fences make good neighbors.' "

CHAPTER III

Why Do Monkeys Shout and Scream So Much?

As THE SUN CAME UP one April morning in the jungles of Ceylon, a scientist settled himself more or less comfortably at the edge of an open clearing right in the middle of four troops of monkeys. The monkeys were gray langurs. They have long tails and can dash about on the ground (on all fours for the most part) or run through the trees at great speed. They have long arms and legs, midnight-black faces and their faces are surrounded by a ring of tawny-to-white fur that ends in a small pointed cap right in the center of the tops of their heads. This makes them look surprised all the time.

The scientist had been studying the gray langurs for months and one of the main reasons for this particular study was to see if the groups ever got into fights with one another. By ten o'clock on this particular morning he had his answer: they sure do.

From the weeks of work that had gone before, the scientist knew the boundaries of the territories of each group. In the case of the langurs, the territories overlapped and the scientist had made careful sketches that showed the sizes of territories and where one ran into another. Group one was on the left side of the forest, Groups two and three had the center—one to the north of the other—while Group four had the right-hand edge of the forest. Group two had the worst of it. It was located in the center on the north edge and its territory overlapped that of Group one and Group four as well as a little part of Group three. The borders of the other groups just barely overlapped each other. The groups varied in size from twelve langurs with two adult males in it to forty-two langurs with six males in it.

So here we have the scientist, notebook in hand, in the clearing, and waiting for the day in monkey life to begin.

For gray langurs, the day starts with a whoop and a holler. When the sunrise wakes them up, the males stretch and yawn a little and then let out a loud "whoop" noise. Aside from helping to wake himself up, the whoop serves another useful purpose. It lets him know where he is (the source of the whoop) and it lets the langurs in neighboring groups know where he is. The whooping not only alerts the langurs, but pinpoints them as well. Probably after several years of whooping in the morning each adult of each group can tell the difference between whoops from one group or individual and another.

The first langur to whoop waits a little while and sure enough there comes an answering whoop from some other group's territory. It is a kind of "we're here and you're over there" message that seems to be passed along. With the four groups in this particular part of Ceylon there had to be a good deal of whooping back and forth before every group seemed satisfied that it was going to be another ordinary day.

As all this early morning whooping is going on, one male

from a group will climb to the top of a tree where he can get a good view of the surrounding countryside. He is a sort of a lookout and he scans the horizon for other langurs. If he has finished his morning whooping, the only noise he makes on sentry duty are low grunts mixed with a strange grating noise which means he is grinding his teeth—like nearly anyone else on sentry duty.

The scientist had watched this sentry-duty routine for some time and had come to the conclusion that the sentry was not up there to warn of tigers or pythons or other langur-eating animals. He was there to keep an eye out for invading langur groups or to spot a group that would be fun to tangle with. Because langurs are often on the alert for a scrap with neighboring groups.

The scientist had also come to another conclusion: the whole subject of territory for animals was a lot more complicated than it appeared to be at first glance. For langurs, unlike tropical fish and dozens of other animals, have a territory but they actually go out of it to get into a good stimulating scrap. Then, the scientist asked, what good is the territory? In this case the group's territories overlapped; poor Group two kept getting beat up but that never affected its territorial size at all. Food was plentiful throughout the forest and water seemed to be no problem—and the territories remained unchanged throughout the study by the scientist. Yet the langurs charged back and forth whooping and hollering to beat the band.

On this particular morning, the scientist was mulling the whole problem over in silence as the whooping part of the day came and went. By eight o'clock that chore was all done. Then the action started.

At ten minutes past eight, two males of Group one lost their cool and raced from the center of their territory to the border chasing six langurs who had invaded. The six were members from Group four—all the way across the forest. These intruders had run right through Group two's range and invaded Group one's. The Group one males chased them back, trampling on Group two going through. Most of Group one turned back but one male finished the job of chasing by standing on a post at the border of Group four's territory and grunting in a very unfriendly manner.

The males of Group four hardly paused for breath after being chased home. They immediately started a fight with the males of Group three and stood on their border slugging it out. They seemed to be getting the better of it so they chased Group three deep into its own territory. This excited poor Group two and its members thought they might win a contest. They began whooping it up in their own territory, daring anyone to run over them again. The langurs in Groups four and three paused to rest a little and then the Group four members pushed Group three even farther from their own borders. In fact they pushed them right into Group one's territory. Then they scampered back to their home field. Group one decided to liven things up so they began to fight with Group four and Group three at the same time. Poor Group two was being attacked by one deformed member of Group three. Group two gave ground rapidly and the attacker from Group three turned his back in disgust and slowly walked away. Nobody chased him.

For a moment the jungle was quiet while everyone caught his breath.

Then it occurred to Group two that they hadn't scored at all that morning. They whooped it up a little and dashed into Group one's territory looking for a fight. They found it. In a flash they retreated. Their small territory was beginning to seem more like an express highway than a snug home. It was humiliating. Could they be losers? They settled down quietly for a period of meditation.

The scientist had tried to take notes during the uproar. But the action took place a little faster than expected. How could orderly notes be taken with gray langurs running around, whooping, leaping through trees, grunting, scampering across the clearing, screaming and gnashing their teeth?

Throughout the field study, the scientist had noted the number of fights between individual groups. The general uproar just witnessed, however, was the only one involving all four groups at once. But it, and all the other fights and chases into and out of territories, proved one thing beyond doubt. Those gray langurs certainly love to fight.

They are not alone. Nearly all primates fight. Baboons, chimpanzees, orang-utans and monkeys of all sorts. One particular small South American monkey was studied for nearly a year in its natural home in the forests of Colombia by a zoologist, William Mason. The monkey is very small—only about one foot high—and is burdened with the name *Callicebus moloch ornatus* but it manages very well. It has auburn-colored hair on its chest and throat and arms. A very visible white band of hair crosses its forehead and some of the monkeys have white gloves and white ear tufts. They do not live in large tribes like the langurs. There is real family grouping among the *callicebus*—an adult pair and one or two youngsters is the rule. The scientist who studied them chose them just because they formed small family groups rather than larger tribes. For his particular subjects, Mason located an isolated stand of forest surrounded by treeless stretches of plains in which nine families of *callicebus* monkeys lived.

Unlike the langurs, the tiny *callicebus* monkeys have very well defined home territories that do not overlap to a great extent. And, like many animals that occupy territories all the time, they have arranged their boundaries and "rooms" within their homes very completely. The bedroom is a single tree to which they go every night to sleep.

Then dawn nudges them awake, they start shouting, too. Their first noise is a kind of moan, just as many humans make on first waking. Then they blow the lid off by going "O-O-O-O" as loud as they can. Sure enough there comes an answering call and then a stream of them as other families greet the morn. Now all nine families are awake. First maneuver is to the bathroom and being tree dwellers this offers no problem. Gravity supplants plumbing. Next to breakfast, and the family moves off to a food tree well supplied with fruit where they feed for awhile.

Then it's off to the fights. A family scampers through the trees to the boundary of its territory and sits waiting for the opposing family to show up. When they do, the two adults

of each pair sit very close together facing each other and re-
peating the early morning calls. Sometimes male and female
of each pair intertwine their long tails in a great show of
togetherness.

After a little more moaning and facing one another, a male
will dash over and chase the male of the other couple. If he
makes a dash and the other does not move, the dashing monkey returns to his mate's side and nothing more happens for
awhile. But if the dashing monkey gets the other male to
retreat, a wild chase follows. Over the trees and into the woods
they go. Leaping among the treetops, running every which
way, they sometimes fall to the ground with a good hard
thump and go running across the ground to a vine or a tree.
If the chasing monkey catches his opponent, the fight is on.
He pushes and slaps his enemy. He may even give him a nip
or two with his teeth—and the defeated monkey runs for a
vine and climbs to safety. Then the dashing monkey returns
to his mate.

These morning fights which seem so important to the monkeys last no more than half an hour. Then it is off to the feeding tree again and perhaps a journey to another side of the
territory where another family of *callicebus* may be found
for another round in the daily fight schedule.

Why a fight schedule? Why a fight at all?

This is one of the biggest questions bothering many kinds
of scientists the world over at this very minute. Biologists, zoologists, physical anthropologists, psychologists, psychiatrists, and
sociologists all have their favorite answers. And in the back

of nearly everyone's mind is the hope that he will find the correct answer, end war among nations and men, receive the Nobel prize and be famous.

Neither the gray langur nor the tiny *callicebus moloch ornatus* monkey cares what the answer is. Nor do tigers, apes, robins, penguins or bumblebees. They simply go on doing what comes naturally and survive very well while man observes their behavior and ponders his own problems, hoping to find a clue in the behavior of animals he thinks are lower than himself.

When fighting among animals is discussed, the word "aggression" pops up. It is a word much in use today both by politicians and anthropologists. Of course they do not mean the same thing when they use the word. Even anthropologists use the word differently among themselves. Psychiatrists may define the word one way, zoologists another and biologists still another. This leads to confusion.

But confusion is nothing new when scientists get together.

Konrad Lorenz, probably the world's leading scientist of animal behavior, defines aggression very simply. He calls it the "fighting instinct in beast and man which is directed *against* members of the same species."

R. L. Holloway, Jr., a physical anthropologist at Columbia University, invokes this definition: "behavior whose goal is the injury of some person or object."

There are many people who use the word "aggressive" and "hostile" interchangeably. The second definition above could lead to that confusion. The first definition, of Mr. Lorenz, might lead to it, depending on the user's outlook on life.

But let's see if there isn't a way to take the "hostility" out of "aggression."

When you read the phrase "war of aggression" there is no doubt that hostility is present—that somebody is out to do somebody in. But when you hear the phrase "an aggressive sales campaign" or "aggressive leadership" the word changes color a little bit. An aggressive salesman may be just an "alert, healthy go-getter"—something admired by people to whom money is life. Is there anything *hostile* about a healthy alert go-getter? Not necessarily.

It may be time now to take a look at the monkeys again. There they are, whooping it up in the trees. The gray langurs commence with their whooping and if this uproar is not enough, they go through what the scientist observer calls "display jumping." When a troop of langurs start this curious behavior, the males of the troop keep whooping and then jump with stifflegged leaps onto lower branches, sometimes even onto dry, brittle ones to make as much foot-thumping as possible. Many times the branches break and the langurs plunge down into the foliage or, on more than one occasion, onto the ground. All the males do this simultaneously and the noise of their jumps mingles with the whooping to produce a frightening sound. Indeed an untrained witness watching the trees shake would probably believe there was a great fight going on. The scientist was amazed at the length and daring of these jumps and he noted that the male langurs were perfectly "in step" and that none got in the way of another, however long or unexpected the leap. They all give the impression of being about to lose their tempers. These display jumps are a threatening gesture on the part of the langurs when another troop is edging into its territory. If the troops meet, the langurs then become aggressive.

Langurs like many monkeys are perfectly capable of biting an opponent to death. And it would seem that if their intent is to injure the invading langurs according to that definition of aggression, then they would immediately leap on them and bite them as severely as possible. No such thing. The males on their territory rush the invading troop. Many times this is enough to discourage the invaders. But if it isn't, then the individuals come to blows—or rather grips—and the langurs wrestle with each other. Only occasionally do they actually bite one another and these are usually superficial bites. Nobody lunges for the jugular vein. The aim, it would seem, is certainly not to kill. In fact it doesn't frequently seem that the aim is even to injure. What is it then?

Take the *callicebus moloch ornatus*. The little tykes enjoy scrapping. Each morning the families go to the edge of their territory and start a fight. But, as has been pointed out, they content themselves with slapping one another and pushing, much like small girls in the third grade.

Observers who have watched aggressive behavior among many animals have been surprised to note that injuries are the exception rather than the rule—even among the snarling tigers of chapter 1. For what they were seeing was ritualized fighting, however noisy and disorganized it seemed to be.

Konrad Lorenz has watched animals long enough to know that they do not follow behavior patterns that are injurious to them or to the species. Many of these animals are what anyone would call aggressive. So the question that occurred to him—and that was answered beautifully in his book *On Aggression* was: what purposes does aggression serve in the survival of a species?

First and, according to Lorenz, foremost on the list is the purpose of spreading the species over as wide a piece of landscape as possible. Combined with the territorial instinct, the aggressive instinct tells the animals to defend the borders of their territory. This assures a food supply for the species and further makes certain that the food supply will be as evenly divided as possible.

Imagine the opposite possibility. If all birds, say, of a species, nested, produced young and fed in the same tree, the food supply would vanish before the young arrived—and, if not then, surely a short time after the eggs hatched. With no instinct to fight among themselves and no instinct to occupy and defend a territory, the birds would soon die, the species become extinct.

Fortunately for the birds, as you know, they do occupy and defend territory and they fight, or threaten to fight, each other. In this process they nest in separate places and defend, depending on their strength and the strengths of their mates, a territory whose size reflects the power of the mating pair.

Observers have noted the same activity among fish of the aggressive and territorial variety. In a given space (say an aquarium) two fish of the same fighting species will divide that space according to their relative strengths. And it is interesting to note that when one fish is given a mate and they pair, that the combined strength of the pair increases their territory. They both fight to defend it. Another curious link between territory and aggressive instinct has been discovered. If two neighboring males in adjoining territories start to fight, the outcome does not depend as much on the relative size and strength of the fighters as it does on just where the fight takes place. If A is larger and stronger than neighbor B, he may invade B's territory and begin the scrap. At first he seems to be winning as he pushes B further and further back into B's territory.

But then a curious thing happens. As B is driven deeper into his home territory, he seems to gain strength. And A seems to lose the will to fight. Soon B is chasing A out of his territory. He may then be so full of fight that he chases larger and stronger A into A's territory. And then the whole procedure reverses again. A becomes stronger and B weaker. It becomes a seesaw battle, a kind of swinging pendulum. A balance and harmony are somehow established—even amid the uproar of the battle.

In Chapter two, the large strange dog wandered into the home dog's territory and didn't even put up a fight. He just ran. And if the second dog had chased the first onto his own home territory, the situation would have been completely turned around.

Scientists have long recognized this curious relationship between ferocity of fighting and nearness to home.

A second purpose served by the aggressive instinct is the matter of selection of mates. Fighting among males for female approval is called the rival fight. It occurs, naturally enough at the mating season and the winner of the fight is adjudged by the female or females of that species to be superior and therefore acceptable as a mate. She (or shes) pair with winners of rival fights. Here, as might be guessed, the classical Darwinian phrase "survival of the fittest" comes to mind. And it is true to a limited degree. But the question of what happens to the loser of the rival fight remains unanswered. Is he killed by his opponent? Since all the tigers aren't dead, the answer is no. The weaker one retreats and may fight again with some other male rival. Again the winner is selected by the available remaining females—and so on. The fights continue until the mating season is over. The complete loser—who has found no mate during the time the females are receptive to male advances simply does not produce offspring. But he isn't killed by the other male members of the species. And the next year, if, for example, he is a young male and simply not strong enough to win a rival fight, he may gain a female and produce young. Here then is an obvious and natural and "moral" method of insuring species survival—by fighting.

A third purpose of aggression is defending the young of the species against attack. Males and females (sometimes together and sometimes singly) will attack any creature, even one of their own species, that comes near or threatens the young. This form of aggression has the blessing of even the least-thinking human male or female—but it is, nonetheless, the same fighting instinct that is frowned on by many people when directed elsewhere.

A fourth display of aggression has equal support from every-

one and that is aggression in support of one's own existence—
or self-defense among both animals and men. Such fighting
behavior may not be thought of as aggression. Yet if Konrad
Lorenz's definition of aggression is acceptable (and here extended to include fighting with *any* attacker) then it can be
mentioned. Many animals would ordinarily like to flee the
scene of an encounter rather than fight. In fact to most animals
there frequently appears to be a choice to be made. If they
come upon a larger, stronger member of their own species—
or a feared member of some other species—they may choose
to avoid a fight by running. But if they are surprised by such
an enemy or are cornered so they cannot run, they fight with
a ferocity seldom seen in other fights. In fact it is here, when
an animal is cornered and when its enemy approaches and
steps over an invisible (to us) line called the critical distance
that a fight to the death may easily occur. After all, what choice
has the cornered animal but to fight to the death? It knows,
or believes, that death at the hands (or claws) of its enemy is
imminent and thus a fight of desperation is the only path of
action left to it. Remember the Alamo?

Unfortunately, men have only lately recognized this. And
many of the films showing the death struggle of animals are
made by forcing the animals into corners where they have to
fight, one or the other is killed or so seriously wounded that
they can no longer defend themselves. Among the few humans
who have long acknowledged the existence of "critical distance" as a trigger to a bloody, final fight, are wild animal
trainers. If they had not recognized it, there would be no wild

animal trainers around to discuss the matter. They stay outside the critical distance until the lion or tiger is thoroughly used to their approach.

Aggression has other important purposes within a tribe or troop of animals. Not the least of them is the fixing of a ranking order among the male members of such a tribe. When rival fights have established the fact that baboon A is the best fighter, baboon B the next best—and so on—the inner peace of the tribe is assured. Baboon B would not think of fighting with baboon A again (at least not until next mating season) and so he obeys baboon A. But baboon B is second in command and expects all lower order baboons to respect his position. In this way a tribal ranking order grows and everyone knows who he is and where he stands. This reduces needless fighting in an established group and promotes group security. More important for the tribe's survival and particularly for the survival of weaker members, when the group is threatened from outside, the stronger members protect the weaker ones. Indeed in some species they form a circle and place the females and weaker older males out of harm's immediate way.

Here again we have what seems at first glance to be a contradiction of Darwin's "survival of the fittest" phrase. Here is a case where the fighting instinct, the aggressive instinct, actually protects the weaker members of a species.

Remember poor Group two among the langurs? The losers who kept getting trampled in the rush? That group, as the observer discovered, had only recently formed. It had only two adult males in it (the smallest number in any of the groups studied). It also had several sub-adults and while the uproar was proceeding over the months of observation the scientist noted that two sub-adults left the group and joined Group one. The group, in fact, did not have the strength to defend its territory completely and it was a new group—this accounts for its weakness. But even in its weakness, it was not destroyed nor was its small territory taken away from it. The other langurs allowed it to survive.

It seems that this thing called aggression is being turned around and becoming something the word does not mean. The answer, according to Konrad Lorenz is: indeed so. It remains an instinct to fight members of one's own species, but from Lorenz's observation of fish and birds, this same fighting instinct is used by nature to form the deepest bonds of comradeship that any animals can know.

He observed, for example, a territory-defending male fish. It attacked every other fish of the same species that approached its borders. Indeed it swam back and forth along the invisible line of its territorial border actually patrolling it against invasion. When another male crossed the line a fight began and the invading male fish fled. But then a female crossed the line. The male rushed at her, displaying its fins and colors in a threatening gesture. The female left in a hurry at that first attack. But she returned. Again the attack by the male. This time the female started to swim away but hesitated. She made a gesture of submission and then swam away a little farther—looking coyly over her scaly shoulder. As this performance was repeated over and over, the male finally became used to the female and she did not arouse his aggressive instinct. Then she made herself at home in his territory and her shyness and fear seemed to disappear almost as soon as she moved in. She took over a joint ownership in the territory and hovered in the middle of it with fins outspread, displaying her colors—giving all the signs of spoiling for a fight. This made the male angry and he responded by flipping out his fins and giving all indication of taking up the fight. They had already formed a bond but, at this point it seemed they were about to get a divorce. The two of them swam broadside to one another and the male flicked his tail several times sending the pulses of energy through the water to strike her. Next he turned and swam toward her exactly as if he were going to ram her—which would have been the most severe and serious blow he could strike. There was no appearance of a ritual fight here. He seemed to mean business. But at the very last second, while she was waiting to be hit, he turned aside and swam to the border of their territory where he started a fight with a neighbor. His aggression has been redirected to act on some object other than his mate.

This action on the part of both fish was repeated over and over—and the pair bond was made stronger. The redirected aggressive motions continued but they had become "greeting" motions. To the untrained observer they were hard to distinguish. In higher forms of animal life similar behavior has been seen. It becomes, however, much more elaborate and when one of a pair of geese comes home to the nest, there is an elaborate greeting ceremony—much head-bobbing, neck twisting and gabble going on. What had been aggression, became, through very complex mechanisms, an important greeting ceremony. In fact, if a partner does *not* go through the greeting ceremony upon entering the homestead, chances are a real fight will break out. By being "rude" enough to ignore the custom of polite greeting, one member of a pair will be actually asking for a beating.

This same kind of behavior mechanism holds for men as well. Imagine walking into a roomful of your friends and saying not a word, ignoring outstretched hands or refusing to smile and nod in greeting. The first reaction on the part of your friends would be anger. Aggressive feelings would be roused in them and the meeting would be off to a bad start. But by taking time to go through the greeting ceremony, the bond of friendship is strengthened and everyone feels better toward one another.

It seems silly now to ask the question: is man an aggressive animal? There is no doubt that he is. And much of what we call human accomplishment was accomplished just because of man's self-assertive, aggressive quality or drive. But the real question today that hangs in the back of everyone's mind is: does this aggressive drive lead to war, to mass killing, to the threat of man's wiping himself and every other living creature from the face of the planet?

An answer comes later but now it can be said that the aggressive instinct has something to do with war. It is not, however, the most important ingredient in man's nature for worldwide destruction. How, all by itself, could a species-preserving instinct like aggression threaten the extinction of the species?

We might here want to recall the two definitions of aggression

1) The fighting instinct directed against members of the same species
2) Behavior whose goal is the injury of some person or object.

Knowing what we now do about the role of aggression among many species of animals, which definition indicates that aggression, by itself, is "bad?"

The key word in the first definition is "fighting"
The key word in the second one is "injury"

The purpose of aggression is not injury but species survival. But if words are used carelessly—as they often are—you might hear the word hostility used in place of aggression. And hostile behavior *does* indicate a desire to injure.

See how complicated it gets?

CHAPTER IV

Do Penguins Really Care?

THE QUESTION: do penguins really care? was answered long ago in one of the most extraordinary adventures that men have ever had.

The answer came as the result of a journey across the wind-swept ice of the Antarctic in the nearly complete darkness of the long polar night. Of course the men had other reasons for studying penguins. Among animals living on earth today, the penguin is one of the most interesting from a scientific point of view. It is a bird that cannot fly. It is primitive in its evolution and represents a link between reptiles and birds which evolved from reptiles. In a way, the penguin provides a window into the past for the scientist, showing him a form of life that has been extinct for millions of years. Most primitive of the penguins is the Emperor penguin, largest of its species.

Until 1901, no one knew anything about the Emperor penguin. They had been seen on ice floes or on ice attached to the shores of the Antarctic continent. But their habits, their life cycles, their structure remained unknown.

In the year 1901, the English explorer Robert Scott sailed to the Antarctic on his first expedition. With him was a medical man and naturalist, Dr. E. A. Wilson. Dr. Wilson had a variety of interests and among them was a desire to learn more about the primitive bird, the penguin. As the expedition ship sailed along the ice barrier in the Antarctic Ocean next to the continent itself, Dr. Wilson spotted a great crowd of penguins and immediately asked permission to go onto the ice to examine them. As he approached the group, he saw they were the very large and little-known Emperor penguins. He also saw that this gathering place was a rookery or breeding ground of the birds.

The location was near a point of land called Cape Crozier which was on Ross Island connected to the continent by the ice barrier. When Dr. Wilson landed he hoped to find unhatched penguin eggs to take as specimens for later study.

He wanted eggs because much can be learned of the formation of an animal from study of it in the embryonic stage of development. But the doctor was disappointed on that trip. All eggs had hatched and there were fuzzy penguin chicks cheeping about on the ice. Dr. Wilson and his party marked the rookery physically with a mound of stones on nearby land. He marked it mentally for a return trip.

That return trip came in 1910 when Scott returned to the Antarctic. Dr. Wilson was with him again and he proposed a most extraordinary project. With the penguin eggs still on his mind, he asked permission to plan a winter journey from the expedition base at Cape Evans on the western shores of Ross Island around the island's fringe on the ice to Cape Crozier. It was a risky undertaking.

At the latitude of the camp on Cape Evans, the polar night is not the legendary six months of darkness. But there are weeks on weeks when the sun does not rise above the northern horizon. There are storms and low temperatures that sometimes reach seventy degrees below zero, Fahrenheit. Dr. Wilson knew all this. He believed, however, that the reward would be worth the risk.

At that time, in 1910, Antarctic exploration was also pioneering. Equipment, methods of hauling supplies, ways of protecting oneself against the hostile environment were all being tested for the first time in many cases. No one knew much about the problems men would face on a long journey. More to the point, no one had traveled on the Antarctic continent in the depths of winter before.

Even today, with all our knowledge of conditions, all our technical equipment, no party undertakes a sledging journey in the middle of winter on the Southern Continent. Only in emergencies does a dog team leave a base camp in that blackness, in that cold.

The distance that Dr. Wilson proposed to cover was not great and this, as much as anything, led him to believe that it could be done successfully. The path he planned to travel measured less than a hundred miles. He chose two companions, Lt. H. R. Bowers and Apsley Cherry-Garrard.

He loaded two nine-foot sledges with all the supplies and equipment needed to last them the journey as well as to preserve the penguins embryos and eggs for later study. Five days after midwinter day (June 22nd) the three men lashed up, slipped the sledge traces around themselves and left Cape Evans.

From the first, things began to go wrong, or at least not

according to plan. The sledges were hard to haul and the men hit a snow surface that increased the friction on the runners so much they could not move both sledges at once. They had to haul one ahead, then backtrack for the other one.

Temperatures dropped and the wind froze the perspiration inside their protective clothing. Within a day or so, their clothing was soaked. Outside the tent it froze solid; inside, when thawed, it was a water-logged mass.

They got off course and wandered into crevasses and high pressure ridges of ice over which the sledges had to be dragged.

And all of it was in nearly total darkness. The only light that came to them from the sky those first days was that of the stars and the moon on clear nights.

Day after day they struggled forward, and sometimes their mileage was pitiably small: two and a half miles; three miles; two miles.

When at last they reached Cape Crozier, they built an igloo of ice blocks and rock and roofed it with canvas tarpaulin. Outside the igloo they pitched their tent. A blizzard came on them after only one brief afternoon among the Emperor penguins. The roar of that wind that pinned them down in the igloo was, according to Cherry-Garrard's description "like the roar of an express train as you pass through a tunnel with the windows down." The tent blew away (their only shelter for the return trip); the tarpaulin was torn off the igloo. The three men in their sleeping bags lay beneath snow for two days and two nights while the winds blew. They were unable to prepare a meal—unable to do anything but kick their feet to combat frostbite and occasionally shove the snow off themselves. Without the tent, with the igloo roof gone and with their oil and food supplies running low, they thought themselves dead men.

When at last the storm blew itself out, they struggled in the drifts (still in their sleeping bags) to light the cooker and heat some food. When that was done, they started a hopeless search for the tent. No one had spoken of the problem but they each knew they could not make the return journey without it.

To their amazement they found it almost undamaged. Instead of ballooning up and blowing north across the waters of the Ross Sea to be lost forever, it had collapsed and been driven down an ice slope where it was wedged between ice hummocks.

With one tin of oil for cooking left and with only one sledge, the three men started homeward. So exhausted were they that they fell asleep while walking and stumbled against one another. Their clothing and sleeping bags were in tatters. Frostbite of hands and feet were the least of their worries on that torturous trip home. One man's teeth were gone and all the nerves killed. Yet this man, Cherry-Garrard, wrote in his diary when they neared the end of their journey ". . . the temperature had risen to $-43°(F)$. We could almost feel it getting warmer. . . ."

And they made it back to Cape Evans after five weeks with three penguin eggs.

* * * * *

While the men were at Cape Crozier they had only a few brief moments to observe the Emperor penguin and gather eggs. By the time they reached the Cape there were but a few hours of daylight each day—or rather a dim sort of twilight often darkened by a layer of clouds. It was during this period the day before the great blizzard pinned them in the igloo that the three men crawled and stumbled down the ice slopes toward the rookery. The first time they tried it they were beaten by the darkness and had to return to their camp and wait for another day. And even then it seemed they would fail. They moved toward the sea ice and found their way blocked by a huge ice pressure ridge that rose vertically above them. From the other side they could hear the penguins calling. They were about to admit defeat when Dr. Wilson discovered a small tunnel carved out by melting ice under the pressure ridge. Into it the eager naturalist crawled. By bracing his back against the ice at the top of the strange opening and pushing his feet on the rocky bottom, he managed to shove through. Bowers followed him and then Cherry-Garrard.

Breathless, the three men stood on the sea side of the pressure ridge and a few hundred yards away on the sea ice were the penguins. The strange figures caused a flurry of activity among the birds and the men advanced cautiously, trying to see as much as they could, to find eggs and get a specimen penguin or two without frightening the hundreds of birds they had found.

The Doctor's original calculations had been correct. The Emperors were protecting eggs of the next generation. And they did this in a most curious way. Each bird with an egg incubated it by holding it on its feet. The downy breast of the bird drooped down over it, enfolding it in a flap of loose skin that had been grown especially for the purpose. The penguins always stood with their backs to the wind to protect the egg. And they would stand for days and nights without food. When at last the pangs of hunger forced a penguin to leave an egg unprotected against the cold and wind, another would pick it up instantly—for many penguins were eggless, having lost or crushed them by mistake. Both the male and female penguin had the same egg-protecting instinct. So harsh is the winter night on the shores of the Antarctic that this deep instinct extends to both sexes. And an eggless penguin, during that season, looks constantly for an egg to hold on its feet. Those with eggs occasionally scuffle about, more awkward than ever with the egg on their feet, and from time to time an egg rolls off. Then there is a fight. Any eggless penguin rushes to pick up the egg. The bird that dropped it rushes to pick it up, too. They actually fight over it and frequently break the egg while fighting. Wilson and his companions searched among the penguins for eggs and found an astonishing thing. On one occasion, Wilson reached for an egg that a startled penguin had dropped and rose from the ice with a round, smooth lump of ice—looking very much like an egg. So strong is the maternal instinct that an eggless penguin will try to hatch out ice rather than give up the fight.

Early, on his previous expedition, Wilson had wondered why the Emperor penguin produced eggs at the coldest, darkest time of the year. In other birds and animals the production of the next generation occurs in spring when temperatures have warmed somewhat. Not so the Emperor.

Wondering about it, Wilson found the solution when he realized that the life cycle of the Emperor penguin is so long that if a bird were hatched in the spring it would not be covered with enough feathers by the time the next winter came. The penguin chicks would surely freeze to death. So the birds breed in midwinter and by nursing the chicks through the next full summer, assure them of enough growth to give them protective feathers with which to face the following winter.

With all the care they receive, a penguin chick leads a dangerous life. As an egg, it might be crushed when older penguins fight for the privilege of holding it. As a very young chick, the same thing may happen. And the chick must be fed and protected long after it is out of its shell. Wilson estimated that only about one out of four eggs produced young chicks— and not all of the chicks grew to adulthood. The mortality rate is high.

There are a few species of birds that inhabit the Antarctic continent or its fringes—the Adelie penguin, a small relative of the Emperor; the snowy petrel; and the skua gull. Of these the Emperor is the only one that breeds during the winter and spends its entire life no farther north than the edge of the pack ice that rings the Antarctic shores. A mysterious creation, the Emperor is so well adapted to its harsh home that it can make use of the storms that sweep off the continent and blow the ice out to sea. When it is time for the penguin to begin its short northward migration to the pack ice, it waits until all the weather signals indicate a storm is coming. Then, with the chicks cheeping beside them, the Emperor penguins waddle to the edge of the ice shelf where the rookery is located. They crowd together on the very lip of the ice and as the storm strikes and the rising seas batter the ice edge, a piece will break off. Winds will take it northward across the water and a group of penguins will sail away on their ship of ice, upright, quiet, and dignified as usual. The rest of the year will be spent on the permanent belt of ice that floats hundreds of miles north of their rookery. The young chicks will develop and learn to fish. They will grow feathers and fatten up enough to live through the next winter when the entire group returns to the rookery for another winter.

Probably no other group of animals has as hard a time raising the next generation of its species safely to a point where the young can take care of themselves. The answer to the question: do penguins really care? must be a loud "Yes."

* * * * *

There are some animals that are born with all the necessary equipment to leave the spot immediately. But these are usually animals that are fairly low on the ladder of evolution. Fish and eels, for example, leave "home" very shortly after they are born and it is lucky that so many are born because they are eaten by other animals of the sea from the moment they begin wiggling a tail. Enough survive, of course, to assure the survival of the species itself.

Others, like the Emperor penguin, have a tougher time. In Chapter Two the idea of territory was shown to have the important purpose, in many cases, of assuring the safe arrival and feeding of each new generation.

But there is more than a simple piece of geography needed to assure the raising of the young in many animal and bird species. Among the most important of the "other" things is the maternal behavior of the female. In the case of some species hard-pressed for survival, the maternal instinct is shared with the male and they both enter the food gathering and, in the case of Emperor penguins, the nest sitting—if you can call a perfectly flat ice sheet a nest.

After eggs hatch in many species of birds there is a time of nest sitting or brooding that is necessary for the survival of the chicks. So the female bird sits on the nest, covering the small birds (who frequently are hatched without fuzz or feathers). But of course, the small ones get hungry and like all animals the world over, they make their hunger known by yelling. In their case it is a cheeping sound but the message is the same.

The female bird is now faced with a dilemma. She must get food, but she must also keep the baby birds warm. She flies quickly from the nest, grabs the nearest worm or insect, and flies back to the nest. If it is not too damp or cold, the little birds are still all right. She feeds them and then covers them again with her body. But soon the same problem arises and she has to repeat her food-hunting expedition. In some species, the male bird assists in the endless task of gathering food in his territory and bringing it to the young.

The kingfisher has been seen by many people flying from the surface of a lake or stream with a small fish in its beak. Naturalists who have watched these birds carefully can tell whether or not they are birds raising a new batch of baby kingfishers. If the kingfisher is fishing for itself, it rises from the water with the fish's head held in its beak and the tail waving about in the air. The bird may disappear in the foliage but the naturalist knows the fish is for his or her own eating— because kingfishers swallow the fish head first. If, on the other hand, the fish is for the fledglings in a hidden nest, the bird rises from the water with the tail of the fish in its beak and the head waving outward—already in position to be swallowed by junior.

Eliot Howard who made such extraordinary observations over half a century ago watched the struggle of the two instincts in a mother bird: the instinct to brood and the instinct to gather food for her young.

In some cases an accident of weather killed the young. Howard wanted to discover what the effects would be on young birds on cold damp days when they were left unprotected while the female searched for food. He got his chance early one June in watching yellow buntings who were nesting not far from his home. The female had no instinct to warn her that cold weather would harm her fledglings if she were gone too long in search of food. He arrived at the nests around five in the morning to find the adult birds off the nests. The young were cheeping hungrily and looked well enough. In a short while the female came back and sat on the nest for awhile, after feeding the young. But she left again very soon on that cold morning and was gone quite a long time. The young birds became noticeably feebler as the minutes ticked away. Finally both birds returned. The female sat on the nest a short while warming the birds and then left again. The temperature was about 49°F and Howard went close to the nest. The young birds were quite feeble and before the female returned again, one had stopped moving. By the evening of that day three of the four baby birds had died. Howard noted that the female still brooded her family, responding to the deep maternal instinct. But she also regularly responded to the other instinct of searching for and returning with food for her young. Only one bird was alive that night when Howard went home. The next morning, it, too, was dead.

Had the temperature been a few degrees higher, the birds would have lived. Howard concluded that with temperatures of 52°F and higher, the resistance of the baby birds permits them to survive while the female gathers food.

During the raising of very young birds, the mother in particular is responding to a number of instincts. The most noticeable one—and probably the most important for the survival of the young—is the aggressive instinct. Few people have not witnessed the aggression of the mother birds as intruders purposely or accidentally come toward their nests. They will, it seems, fight anything. Mother robins will rise up in wrath against hawks, crows, or jays that threaten their young. In other times, the female robin would not think of attacking the larger birds.

This aggressive instinct of motherhood has long been a subject of admiration among naturalists who see it and readers who read about it. And a great many books have been written about it and have carried the idea too far. Often the most spellbinding part of such a courageous story has to do with the mother bird or animal sacrificing her life for her young. This rarely happens. If the intruder is much larger than the mother animal and if the mother is not armed by nature to deal successfully with such an intruder, she leaves her nest or burrow and in so doing leaves her young defenseless.

If the aim of all these instincts is the preservation of the species, and most evolutionists believe it is, then the fleeing mother cannot be accused of cowardice. An overpowering intruder would kill both her and her present brood. Then she could produce no more young. By fleeing, she loses one brood—but there is always another spring and another brood to raise.

If, on the other hand, the intruder is what the mother feels is of manageable size, she will attack with a fury that is rarely equalled in animal fights.

This blind attacking instinct which is at its height when the mother is brooding raised long ago the question: how does the mother recognize her own chicks? And in one curious experiment an answer came back that astonished everyone.

The experimenters in this case were Wolfgang and Margaret Schleidt. Like thousands of scientists before them, they were working on one question when they received an answer to another. The object of their original research was to test the reaction of male turkeys to certain sound stimuli. One part of the experiment called for them to observe differences in reaction between turkeys that could hear and those that couldn't. Since there are few deaf turkeys running around, the researchers had to make them deaf and this they did by way of an operation on baby turkey chicks.

Since the sex of a small turkey chick is difficult to discover, they simply took a handful of chicks and performed the operation on all of them. They knew some females would be deafened but that appeared to be no problem. They already had another experiment up their sleeves that would involve deaf turkey hens.

When the deaf hens grew up they let them brood like all the others. They were aware that the call of the mother hens had something to do with the response of the wandering chicks. In other words, when chicks cheeped and a turkey hen called in response to the cheeping, some communication was going on because the chicks always rushed to their home beneath mother hen.

They thought the deaf hens, unable to hear the cheeping, would call in some aimless way and at any old time while the hens that could hear the cheeping would reveal a pattern or call note that would be the signal to come home.

So the eggs hatched and shortly thereafter the chicks were out and cheeping. The researchers watched breathlessly and what they saw was very upsetting. The deaf hens responded to the cheeping chicks by pecking them to death almost immediately. All maternal behavior seemed to have been destroyed by their deafness. And then it dawned on the Schleidts that the mechanism by which a mother turkey hen recognizes baby turkey chicks is the sound of their cheeping alone. It is the *only* way she can recognize them.

This new discovery led to further experiments. Turkey hens that could hear were used to test the idea the Schleidts had come across. A dummy chick, looking just like a live one, was pulled by a string within pecking distance of a brooding hen with perfect hearing. As soon as the dummy got close enough, she pecked it as hard as she could. Yet when a small transmitter was put inside the dummy and turned on to a tape recording of chick cheeping, the mother hen accepted the dummy as her own. Neither shape nor size nor color are used by turkey hens to identify their young. It is sound alone.

To back up their data even further, the Schleidts placed the cheeping transmitter in a dummy skunk and pulled that hated enemy of hens closer and closer to the mother hen with the cheeping going full blast. The mother hen called and clucked and raised her wings taking the skunk under the shelter of her body just as if it were a chick—which it was, to her.

These and many other experiments with different animals have led ethologists to suspect the idea of a complex collection of instincts lumped under the one word "maternal." In the case of the turkey hen, the basic instinct of aggression becomes more and more obvious as the brood hen hatches her chicks. It will be used against anything that moves (so long as whatever moves is not big enough to threaten her own life). It would be used against her own chicks except for the one checking mechanism, the one thing that inhibits her from killing her chicks: the sound of their cheeping.

Defense of the nest and eggs by many birds is not attacking what moves but rather remaining absolutely motionless and quiet. This is particularly true of birds most people would call "shy." These are camouflaged birds who often rely on becoming invisible to survive. In one instance the writer came across a nest of the Least bittern, as shy and camouflaged a bird as you can find. The hen had been observed before the nesting season but only from a distance of not less than fifty feet. Her home territory was a long line of rushes and cattails bordering the shore of a Florida lake. At dawn and dusk she could be seen winging her silent, dipping way to other shores for feeding, but during midday when the light was strong she was difficult to find. By drifting silently along the line of cattails in a rowboat, I learned to locate her by sight, sitting quietly in the cattails, her beak held straight into the air and neck extended so that the untrained eye would slide past what it might see as a dry light brown cattail stem.

And then for a few days she disappeared. Nowhere along the shore could I see her nor did she fly in the evening twilight across the water as before. Somewhat worried (and ignorant) I rowed the boat toward her favorite location about midway along the line of rushes, shipped oars and allowed the bow of the boat to move softly into the cattails. I then crept forward to have a really close look around. As I was watching my step over the concrete block which served as an anchor, there was a sudden scurry within a few feet of the boat. I glanced up to see the bittern struggling off through the cattails, one wing fluttering and the other dragging along.

Alarmed by her injury, I backed the boat out and followed her. She watched from a leaf to which she was clinging and when I approached she fluttered and dragged her way a few feet farther on. All my sympathies were roused now and I followed her until she had led me a hundred yards along the shore. Then, to my open-mouthed astonishment and education, she rose in the air leaving her fake injury behind and flew as gracefully as ever across the lake. It took a few moments to realize I had been fooled and when I recovered from that feeling, I rowed back to the original spot. Standing in the bow of the boat I found the nest with three light blue and brown-speckled eggs in it—kept warm by the spring sunshine.

Had the intruder been a natural enemy of hers, approaching to kill her or rob the nest of eggs, she would have drawn the enemy away from the nest just as she had me. He would have thought an easy meal was within reach and followed her. If he got too close she would rise, just as she had for me and fly away, saving both herself and the eggs.

All the instincts of the females that serve to insure the survival of the species might be lumped under the heading "maternal" but some ethologists have shown that there is no one maternal instinct. Aggression, fear, flight (with deception thrown in) or fight are all working toward the single end: survival to assure a new generation.

Among the questions that have come up in the entire study of this phase of animal behavior is: how do the young recognize their parents?

In some species of animals, like the Emperors, it does not matter which adults are the actual parents. Any adult will respond to the begging of a young member of the species. Among rats, for example, any young rat can enter the nest of a female rat and be fed and taken care of—so long as it is from the same group of rats. Among other species of life, some mechanism must work, however, to let the young know exactly who its parents are. Among some birds, for example, a curious and as yet little understood system of recognition actually seems to imprint the image of the actual mother on the young. Ducklings can be so imprinted a very short time after being born. The first thing they see moving—which under normal conditions would be their mother—becomes, for them: MOTHER. And they remained attached to this form for as long as they need to develop into self-sufficient animals. Some curious things have happened as a result of this.

If a duckling sees a man walking by an incubator, it will

attach itself to that man and follow him wherever he goes. The man becomes MOTHER.

One zoologist who was studying animal behavior was driven nearly out of his mind by a duckling that became imprinted and took him to be mother. The zoologist would go to his office to work and look down. Between his feet would be the duckling, snuggled up and preening itself happily. This made the zoologist so nervous he could not work. If he moved a foot without looking, he could squash the duckling. Wherever the man went, the duckling followed. It followed him to work, to meals, outside, inside. It even insisted on sleeping in bed with him. If the man put it in a closed box, it cheeped until he couldn't stand that any more and then he would take it back to bed for the sake of peace and quiet. Each time the man pushed the duckling away, its cheeps broke his spirit and he allowed the duckling back. Finally in desperation he called a friend who was going on a trip and asked if he would take the duckling to a zoo. The friend thought the zoologist was acting rather silly about it all but he did the favor. By the time the friend had driven half a mile, the duckling was out of the box and sitting on his lap—preening contentedly. He had attached himself to a new MOTHER. The journey turned into a nightmare and the friend finally transferred the duckling's affections to a lady research assistant at the zoo. *She* spent several sleepless nights teaching the duckling that its place was in a box under her bed, not on the pillow beside her.

The entire mechanism of "imprinting" as it is called is not yet fully understood. But there is no doubt that it occurs. Ducklings have been hatched and the first thing they have been permitted to see has been a moving box. This becomes MOTHER, to the duckling. Chicken eggs have been hatched with duck eggs and the young chickens, seeing the mother duck as the first moving thing, attach themselves to her. They will even follow her into the water until they suddenly realize they are not very good swimmers. They return to dry ground and stand at the water's edge calling plaintively until the duck returns with her true ducklings.

There is no question but that penguins really care—and turkey hens and rats and ducklings. But it would seem that each animal's caring is only a response to something "mechanical" like an instinct. This disappoints many people—who like to believe that other animals are just like themselves, only not quite so bright. But while it disappoints them, it gives them a feeling of being better than all other animals. The lower animals, as many people fondly think of them, are not able to form friendships, close attachments and certainly not capable of feeling anything as human as love. Or can they?

CHAPTER V

Can Geese Fall in Love?

JOHN MUIR was more than a great American naturalist and conservationist. He was a great natural man. By natural man, I mean one who spent most of his life in contact with nature. As a result, Muir had more knowledge about the numberless strange processes that make up the fabric of life on our planet than most men of his time. His time, not at all incidentally, was one during which men actually believed they had learned everything about the universe and that there was little left to discover.

John Muir was born in 1838 and died in 1914. During the middle and late-middle part of the nineteenth century (from about 1850 to 1890) the so-called-mechanistic sciences of physics and chemistry had produced such startling results in commerce and manufacture that men settled down with an insufferably smug look on their faces to enjoy life. Newton had discovered the basic laws of mechanics in physics long before; Watt, Faraday and others had added their discoveries, and it seemed, to the shortsighted men of that time, that at last the universe had yielded its final secrets.

And, so the argument went, since man had done the discovering, man must be the superior being and what he invented and produced were the best things conceivable. All of nature —animals, plants, and minerals—was regarded as something to be used by men, exploited and exhausted or thrown away.

Of course, John Muir as a small boy on his father's farm in Wisconsin did not know all this. His world was limited to the physical horizons of the farm, the dark woods, and cleared fields that he, his father and younger brothers worked from dawn to dark; to the animals on the farm and in the forests and to the few remaining smallpoxed Indians who occasionally drifted out of the dark woods to ask for handouts and then vanished into the darkness from which they would never return.

During a long day in the fields, young John Muir had a lot of mental energy to spend, for while plowing a field with a yoke of oxen is hard physical work, it does little or nothing to use up mental energy. And Muir had a lot of it. He observed the world around him as keenly as any modern ethologist.

At an early age he rejected the religion of his family. They were Scotch Presbyterians and whatever the beliefs of that denomination may be today, in Muir's day and in his family they meant to work yourself—or preferably somebody else— to death in order to get rich. His father, therefore, tried to work his son to death. Not at all oddly, John resented this. So he mentally and emotionally threw out the world of men as he knew it at that time—which meant his father.

To fill the vacuum, Muir began a lifelong love affair of his own with nature. He did not look down on animals as though from a God-given pedestal. He looked at them as his close friends and companions. He also looked at them with a very keen, first-class brain. As a result he saw things that other men could not see.

During the long (sixteen-and seventeen-hour) days of work in the fields, Muir walked behind a plow drawn by a yoke of oxen. Now the Muirs had come from Scotland where there were no oxen and they fascinated the young boys. The animals were used for all the hard work that had to be done on the farm such as ploughing, logging and hauling. As he wrote of the experience:

"We worked with them, sympathized with them in their rest and toil and play, and thus learned to know them better than we should had we been only trained scientific naturalists. We soon learned that each ox and cow and calf had individual character. Old white-faced Buck, one of the second yoke of oxen we owned, was a notably sagacious fellow. He seemed to reason almost like ourselves. In the fall we fed the cattle lots of pumpkins and had to split them open so that mouthfuls could readily be broken off. But Buck never waited for us to come to his help. The others when they were hungry and impatient, tried to break through the hard rind with their teeth, but seldom with success if the pumpkin was full grown. Buck never wasted time in this mumbling, slavering way, but crushed them with his head. He went to the pile, picked out a good one, like a boy choosing an orange or apple, rolled it down on to the open ground, deliberately kneeled in front of it, placed his broad flat brow on top of it, brought his weight hard down and crushed it, then quietly rose and went to his meal in comfort. Some would call this 'instinct' as if so-called 'blind instinct' must necessarily make an ox stand on its head to break pumpkins when its teeth got sore, or when nobody came with an axe to split them. Another fine ox showed his skill when hungry by opening all the fences that stood in his way to the corn fields.

"The humanity we found in them came partly through the expression of their eyes when tired, their tones of voice when hungry and calling for food, their patient plodding and pulling in hot weather, their long-drawn-out sighing breath when exhausted and their enjoyment of rest with the same grateful looks as ours. We recognized their kinship also by their yawning like ourselves when sleepy and evidently enjoying the same peculiar pleasure at the roots of their jaws; by the way they stretched themselves in the morning after a good rest; by learning languages—Scotch, English, Irish, French, Dutch—a smattering of each as required in the faithful service they so willingly, wisely rendered; by their intelligent, alert curiosity, manifested in listening to strange sounds; their love of play; the attachments they made; and their mourning, long continued, when a companion was killed."

What attachments? What "mourning, long continued?"

Many present day scientists on reading John Muir's account of his deeply felt observations would hurl out a word that's getting a lot of use today in life-science circles: anthropomorphizing. This is one of the worst things you can be said to do. What it means, according to the dictionary, is "attributing human form or personality to animals." The real insult intended by someone saying that you are anthropomorphizing is in the first place that you are not being an objective scientist and in the second place everyone but a fool knows that human personality and qualities are superior to those of all other forms of life. So, quicker than you can say "anthropomorphizing," you have been accused of being unscientific and probably a fool.

There are times when the use of the dreadful word is all right. One of them that comes to mind is when some mindless lady trains her small dog to sit up at a dining table and wear a napkin tied around his throat. The feeling then is that the napkin is around the wrong throat and not tied nearly tight enough. Another equally nauseating occasion is the circus or vaudeville act in which monkeys or dogs are dressed as little people and everyone laughs happily at the awkward attempts of the animals to act as humans. A good, semi-scientific example of anthropomorphic tendency can be found in the following kind of logic:

> Human beings use an elaborate language for most of their communication.
> Animals can make a few sounds but cannot talk as we do.
> Conclusion: Animals have an inferior communication system.

In a sense this is backward anthropomorphizing. *Because* animals do not have "our" language they are in that respect "inferior" to man. (And before we leave this small but important point please note that animals rarely misunderstand one another. Whatever their communication system may be, it works better than ours.)

There is a deeper mistake being made, however, in the above example. The assumption has been made that the primary means of communication among animals *ought* to be vocal because it is so in man. This is true anthropomorphizing. (Suppose some of the animal species are telepathic, that is, are mind readers? How would we, not being mind readers, discover this fact?)

So let us allow those who wish, to accuse John Muir of anthropomorphizing. He observed what he called many human qualities in the oxen on his father's farm. He need not have expressed it that way. Suppose he had said that he observed many ox-like qualities in humans: friendship, playfulness, grief. But it seemed natural to John Muir (as it was) to use his own feelings as a basis for comparison; so he said, in effect, "They feel as we do."

A Martian or a bright UFO pilot might observe that all complex forms of life on the planet Earth have some feelings and patterns of behavior in common. In Muir's case, he got so involved with nature that he thought of all animals as "little people." His way of looking at animals finds an echo in a twentieth-century scientist who studied animal behavior and was often accused of being too cold-bloodedly scientific about it. He replied that he was not cold-blooded at all and that he thought of animals as being "very emotional people with very little intelligence."

Since many of us know such people, a word ought to be said here in defense of the scientist's statement. He did not mean it as an insult to the animals.

But doubtless many people still want to feel that only humans can experience love. The word, unfortunately, has as many different meanings as there are people using it so, for the moment, let's not try to define it. Let's just observe what happens.

Courtship

One of the best places to observe courtship is in any public school. Boys and girls start to school at an early age and do not like each other. Then something happens. Boy comes to school one day a little neater than usual. Boy behaves differently. He combs his hair. At night, in the privacy of his room, he surveys his muscles. He clenches them and stands like Tarzan before his mirror. He's out of his mind.

At school he still plays games with the other boys but can often be found straying away from the game and turning up at one particular spot on the sidelines—where one particular girl is located.

He walks back and forth before her. He chews grass stems. He argues with his team captain that he ought to be playing right field rather than left field because he's better there. (She's there.)

In the meantime, particular girl looks the other way. She's cool. But when boy is busy showing off, particular girl is watching. When he finishes showing off and looks to her for acceptance, she is looking somewhere else. He goes farther out of his mind.

Then one day she smiles at him.

Boy's wig crumbles. He runs about leaping fences, hormones hopping all over the place.

Soon boy and girl are seen walking home from school. He's

won. He gets to carry her books. Maybe she will even let him do her homework.

* * * * *

Dr. Paul A. Johnsgard of the University of Nebraska watches ducks. He also watches geese and swans. So far he has watched 138 species of waterfowl.

Here is what he saw when he watched ducks.

In many duck species, the male has brighter and more color-ful feathers than the female. This is true among such North American ducks as mallards, American widgeons, the teals (blue-winged, green-winged, and cinnamon), pintails and others. In all of these ducks, Dr. Johnsgard found that the males had certain motions they went through when they wanted to attract the attention of the female. These motions are different for different species of ducks, so let's concentrate on the mallard. Dr. Johnsgard found that the boy mallard had a particular set of three basic movements he went through to find out if girl mallard really cared.

The three motions are called the "grunt-whistle", the "down-up" and the "head-up-tail-up." The grunt-whistle is sort of a body-shaking motion in front of girl duck accompanied by a whistle. He swims high in the water and the effort makes him grunt. Next, boy duck goes into the down-up motion for his hoped-for girl duck. It is a drinking motion: first, head and bill down into water surface and then neck and head up ver-tically, with more whistles. Then the third act comes on, the head-up-tail-up. In this the mallard struts before girl duck in the water, tail feathers as high as possible, head and neck held proudly up and he displays his colorful wing feathers by raising his wings. More whistles. He makes this display broadside to her so she can see how big and strong he is.

When the performance is over, he faces her and swims by on one side or the other, head bobbing up and down in what is called "nod swimming." To ring the curtain down, the male then turns his head away from the female and shows off the black feathers on the back of his neck.

During most of this hard work on the part of boy duck, girl duck is floating comfortably on the water paying no great attention to him. But she watches him, sometimes literally out of the corner of her eye. And if she decides she likes him, her eyes have a soft expression that he really digs. They swim off together.

No books. No homework.

Male Competition

Boy goes to high school. He's through with all that dumb kid stuff and besides the girl's family has moved to Terre Haute, Indiana so that is that. Besides he is no longer square when it comes to girls. There is this groovy blonde in his biology class and he is going to get her for a date if it's the last thing he does. The trouble is he sees her going out of the high school building with a big red-faced kid who looks dumb as a post but plays tackle on the football team. And he's a senior. Boy must play it cool.

It is plain to see that blonde girl likes football players, so boy goes out for football and gets slaughtered. Third string end. No good. But he grinds through the rest of the season.

At the Christmas dance, he goes stag and cuts in on blonde girl. He has decided to try the intellectual approach. He talks of fallout and blast off and the old, old Beatles.

Blonde girl looks slightly impressed and boy's blood races through his veins, double quick.

Boy cuts in once too often on blonde girl and big red-faced creep objects. After the dance, boy starts home and there is creep.

A group of boys gather around. Red-faced senior thumps boy on the chest with enormous forefinger and tells him to stay away. Boy, scared but not willing to back down, says it's a free country.

"Yeah?"

"Yeah"

Thump and whack.

Boy is flat on his back, in his free country.

Red-faced senior and blonde girl still go together.

* * * * *

Of course these rival fights are tougher for some species than others. When mating time comes to most species there are just about the same number of males as females. This, as you might suspect, is the time when the rival fights break out all over the landscape. And when pairing and mating season has passed, there is less ferocious fighting among the members. They may even abandon territory for a time.

The unhappy males of a species that have not found a mate and paired with her sometimes form a kind of loser's club or bachelor's club, however you want to look at it. Seals do this as do sea gulls among the birds.

But rival fights continue and, for one particular species, it is a year-round proposition. In Uganda, Africa there is a beautiful species of antelope, called the Uganda kob. There are herds of them that number into the thousands. Now the female of the species does not have a particular time of year when the mating drive strikes her. As soon as she has weaned one generation she is prepared to start another.

Early observers of the kob had seen groups of females alongside males in the undergrowth, grazing away, and the assumption was that the girls belonged to him and that when the season came for mating he would perform his duty as males of other species did. No.

An American scientist by the name of Helmet K. Buechner discovered the secret of the Uganda kob's rival fights and mating habits and it is most astonishing. Deep in the interior he found, on a cleared plain, a group of male kob looking as if they were all on display. Each one occupied a small closely cropped green area. Each one stood in the center of it and defended it against all males who tried to invade his small but important territory. There were only a few of these green, cropped territories, no more than fifteen in any area. Each male kob fought all comers. If one territory owner had to leave his piece of ground to go to the stream for a drink, or to a nearby salt lick, he had to fight his way back onto his territory. For during his absence another male would take it over. If the original owner succeeded in regaining his territory then he strutted on it while he and the other territory-holding males awaited the arrival of female kobs.

It became evident to Buechner that these few male kob

occupying territory had to perform the entire mating function for a herd of over 1000. And since the females had no set season for mating, this meant that these male kob had to fight rival males and perform their procreative function on a year-round basis. As if that weren't enough they got into rival fights several times each day. Obviously these kob were the strongest of the species—and just as obviously the males that could not get and defend territory do not breed.

Other species don't have such a strenuous method of producing the next generation. But there are always rival fights. Males, during such fights, can and do inflict injury on their opponents. Even though the male Uganda kob and other normally non-aggressive species stick to a ritual fight, the carnivores with their do-it-yourself weapons of tooth and claw scratch and bite each other, sometimes quite seriously.

Homebuilding

Boy finally *did* find a girl friend. It happened when he was three years out of high school. She was not blonde. But she was *his*. What attracted him to her? Well, he couldn't quite say. But she had, you know, well she was *nice*. Know what he means?

No.

It doesn't really matter. Boy and girl marry. Nice girl takes over after the honeymoon and leads him about in search of a nest or house. Boy gets weary traipsing around after girl. Where does she get the energy? Every corpuscle in her bloodstream drives her to find just the right nest, home.

And at last she finds it.

Boy says, "How do you know this is it?"

Girl replies, "I just know, that's all."

Boy sighs and complies.

*   *   *   *   *

The process of pairing and the timing of all the mating activities is, of course, different for different species. As earlier noted the male bird secured the territory *before* pairing took place. Once that is done, however, the female scurries about selecting an actual location for the nest. What decides her? Who knows the "why" of the female?

One scientist, a Dr. W. H. Thorpe, studied the nest-building process of a particular bird species in England. The bird, he discovered, builds a real house-nest. It has a roof, walls, floor, and front door. At the start, the female hops around among the trees looking for the site. It is always in the fork of a branch but what makes her decide on a particular fork is not known. When, however, she appears to be satisfied with the fork she is inspecting, she begins collecting moss. She flies to the fork with a bit of moss in her beak and places it gently on the fork. Then she flies away for more moss. The bit of moss on the fork falls off. She returns with moss. *It* falls off. Is she discouraged? Not a bit. She keeps bringing moss until she has built a little pile of it on the fork.

Then quick as a flash she darts out and comes back with some used spider silk from spider webs she has spotted in the trees. With these strands she ties down the platform of moss she has produced. Then more moss, which will form the walls and roof of her home. She weaves strands of moss painstakingly with her beak and the fabric of moss grows, made up of vertical and horizontal threads. She has formed a partial cup of moss on top of the platform.

Next the bird flies off and returns with bits of lichen which are attached to the outside of the cup of the nest. To help form the cup, she tramps around in it stamping with her feet; she also presses the curved front of her breast against the cup to give it a perfectly round shape. She continues weaving moss until the walls are nearly up and then starts forming an entry at a convenient place for approaching the nest. She weaves the strands of moss very tightly around the front door so it will keep its shape. Then she continues weaving moss until the dome or roof is completed. Lastly she gathers feathers to line the inside of the nest and make it as soft an interior as possible.

When she is finished, she inspects it proudly. She may even call to her mate to come look at what she has done. And where has he been all the time? Out on the borders of their territory keeping enemies away like any good husband.

Raising the Family

Boy has become assistant manager of the hardware store and also been promised that he will become a partner in the business soon.

All goes well but the nest seems small. What was room enough for two is not room enough for four (small boy, small girl). Man and woman consult about moving to bigger nest. Decide to do so. Visit bank and take on mortgage. Three-bedroom ranch with garage and breezeway.

Boy follows man into woods on long tramps. Learns about baseball. Girl watches mother in kitchen, ties on small apron and stands on a stool to help wash dishes. Girl joins Brownies. Mother is Den mother.

Off to school. Help boy and girl with homework.

Sunday school. Instruction.

"Mommy why do you do that?" "Mommy what is that?"

"Dad, what's the matter with this?" "Hey, Dad. Can you help me . . . ?"

"Junior, if I've told you once, I've told you a thousand times, never. . . ."

"Sweetie, mummy has asked you repeatedly. . . ."

(Late one night) man asks "Is there any reason why he has to act like that?"

Woman smiles. "It's just the way you used to be."

"Hmmmpphh."

All acts, moods, thoughts flow, spoken or unspoken, in a long stream between man-woman parents and boy-girl children. The children are sponges, silently learning, absorbing everything. The shaping and molding go on. On secret levels that no one suspects are there.

One day boy comes home from school with his hair combed. His mother says nothing. She sees him standing in front of his mirror rippling his muscles, like Tarzan.

"He's out of his mind" she thinks—and wonders who the girl is.

*   *   *   *   *

Amoeba are lucky. Comes the time to produce another generation and the two halves of one amoeba wave goodbye and split up. But as the forms of life get more and more complicated, the problem grows. Among all mammals and many birds there is a period of caring for the young who are born quite helpless. They must be fed, diapered, burped, and trained before they can face the wide, cruel world. This may require a very long or a relatively short time.

Two scientists of animal behavior studied the problem of early babyhood relationships between mother and baby of two different types of a particular monkey species (the pigtail macaque and the bonnet macaque, as they are poetically called). They watched selected groups of these two kinds of monkeys during a number of births in each and they were sort of sneaky about it because they didn't want the monkeys to know these intimate home scenes were being observed. They used one way viewing screens in the walls of pens.

In every case they were able to report normal births—mother and baby doing fine, thank you. But there was a curious difference between the mothers' reactions immediately after they gave birth.

The pigtail mothers took their babies and stayed away from all other members of the group for quite a while. If any male or female of the group approached, the mother showed signs of anger and fighting. They were very protective of their infants. The bonnets on the other hand, immediately took their infants over to the other females and showed them off. They let the others fondle the new baby, groom it and generally inspect the addition to the family.

As the weeks passed in each case, the mothers carried the infants cuddled against their own stomachs. The infants clung to the mothers day and night. But then gradually the ties loosened. Soon the baby monkeys were making efforts to leave mother's side. If it happened too early, the mother brought the infant back. But if the infant showed signs of wanting to make a career of being mother's pet, the mother deliberately kicked baby out. If baby tried coming home to mother, mother picked the little rascal up and shook him or gave him a few nips to discourage further homecoming. The change from cradling to kicking out covered many months so there was nothing sudden about it. But when it was time for junior to go, he went.

But how do the youngsters learn everything needed to become successful monkeys? Very much the way humans do: by watching, by being near the parent, by partaking of the invisible stream of knowledge coming in through all the senses.

The running fight between scientists who believe instinct (heredity) is more important in development of offspring and those who feel that one's outside environment and learning from it are paramount is beginning to lose its fury. Learning, in higher forms of life, plays quite a large part in the development of the young. It overlies instinct and, as science knows today, acquired characteristic behavior, over not too many generations may find acceptance in the genetic code of the species and thus become what has been called instinctive behavior.

The Lasting Bond

Many species of birds and animals choose different mates each year. Some pair for life. Among the few birds that mate for life is the goose. They are long-lived animals and the pair, when formed, will last through all the years unless some disaster occurs.

No man alive today knows more about the life and behavior

of geese than Konrad Lorenz. He has observed them so closely that he can astonish visitors by pointing to a goose or a pair or a family and say "Look now. They're going for a swim." And sure enough, with much tail-waggling, the geese waddle to the water and, gabbling among themselves, swim off on the bright surface of the pond. It takes know-how to learn goose talk that well.

To Dr. Lorenz, there is no question but that geese fall in love. Many times he has seen a young gander begin behaving the same way the boy in the schoolyard did. Or as the ducks do.

Observing the geese as he has over the years, Dr. Lorenz has watched a pair of geese produce generations of little geese. The two parents are always in each other's company and if, for any reason, one member of a pair is taken from the vicinity of the other, the goose or gander remaining becomes terribly anxious. The lone goose calls and begins to search for his loved one. The anxiety deepens. The search widens. As time passes and the other member of the pair does not return or is not found, panic sets in. The anxious bird literally becomes panic-stricken —so panic-stricken that he injures himself flying about looking for his mate.

But if the lost one is found, the pair are reunited and the relief and delight are so clearly expressed in their elaborate greeting ceremony that the observer himself sighs with relief.

Over the years, watching the behavior of geese, Lorenz and his assistants have witnessed nearly every kind of marital and romantic entanglement among geese that exists among human beings.

Take the case of a goose falling in love with a married gander. For four years she pursued that gander—not like a brazen hussy but like a true lady. She never caused trouble. She just happened to turn up wherever the gander happened to be. She would casually stroll across his path, love shining in her limpid goose eyes. Ganders, on the other hand do not resemble Heathcliff. They may go for a married goose but if she ignores them for a period of time, give up and look elsewhere.

Then there was the case of the brazen single goose. She did not pair off as a young goose and she spent years having mad, mad affairs with any gander who caught her fancy. She was the scandal of the neighborhood. But then, one day, she gave a newly arrived handsome gander the eye and he responded. The affair was going its usual course, for her, when to her amazement she fell in love with the gander and married him. And she lived happily ever after and became a model mother.

Of course there had to be a case of a straying gander. One married gander seemed to be a model husband. While his wife was tending the eggs on the nest, he would guard the territory and fight off any goose or gander that approached. One goose kept "dropping by", however, to see how things were going. But the gander drove her off just as determinedly as any other. It was thought that he was not falling for her outrageous flirting. One day, to the consternation of the observers, they found this model husband far from the nest in the undergrowth having a wild affair with that flirtatious goose.

And so the cycles of life, under Lorenz's observation, succeeded each other—courtship, pairing, nesting, raising a family.

Inevitably, at some point, a member of a pair will die or be killed accidentally. It is then that these animals show grief of the most unmistakable sort. If it is the gander that dies or is killed, the goose will lose all her enthusiasm for anything. She drops lower and lower in the ranking order of the flock. She stays by herself. More importantly her appearance changes. Lorenz likens it to the show of grief around the eyes that is identical in humans. The eyes sink back into the eye sockets and the result is what we would call "hollow-eyed." A pouch appears beneath each eye and the result is the classic outward expression of grieving.

So, if by love, we humans mean courtship and mating, life-long attachment, joy in mutual companionship, grief upon the death of a lifelong partner, then the answer to the question is "Yes. Geese can fall in love."

CHAPTER VI

Which Dumb Animal?

As YOU KNOW, gray langurs start each day with a loud "WHOOP." This signal or communication can be heard several hundred yards away from the roused animal. The langur's sound is very different from the waking call of the scrappy little *callicebus moloch ornatus* in Colombia which is reported as a long drawn out "O-O-O-O."

Now that we have the age of the tape recorder, stereo and hi-fi, scientists are beginning to use all sorts of electronic tools to record and study the uproar coming from the jungle. From Ceylon to Colombia and back again they lurk in the undergrowth, microphones at the ready, to catch even the intimate sweet nothings spoken by the jungle beasts. The clucks, screams, shouts, and barks are going to be put on the spectrograph whether the animals want it or not. Scientists are pretty sure that all the noises mean something since animals do not make idle sounds. They don't hum to themselves. They don't talk to themselves either.

With all this eavesdropping by scientists, it is safe to say there is a vast listen-in proceeding all along the jungle belt. One scientist spent considerable time recording the noise coming from groups of vervet monkeys in Kenya, East Africa. He carefully analyzed the monkey's talk on the spectrograph and noted the actions of the monkeys, their age, sex, and apparent state of mind when they made the sounds.

In writing up his results, this scientist had to spell out the sounds and this is what some of them became:

Chutter
Squeal
Chutter-squeal
Squeal-scream
Bark
Woof-woof
Waa
Woof-waa
Rraugh (short and long)
Purr
rrr
Rrah
Eh, eh
eee

With this rich vocabulary, the monkeys could say practically anything they needed to communicate with each other. Much depended, according to the scientist, on what the monkey was doing and where he was when he uttered one of the interesting sounds above. A scream might mean one thing if the animal was being pursued by a python; quite another if a young male was chasing a young female. This is not surprising since there is a great difference in the scream of a woman at a cocktail party and in the moment when she loses her footing and sprawls on the sidewalk.

Compared to vervet monkeys, gorillas are hopelessly retarded, at least in terms of the variety of sounds they produce. (They have other means of communicating, up their sleeves however, as we shall see.) In the famous San Diego zoo, two gorillas—Ingagi and Mbongo by name—were observed for communication behavior over a period of time. The only sounds that came out were grunts—long, monotonous series of them. The observers noted that the monotony varied in only two ways. One was in the pitch or frequency of the grunts. When the gorillas were excited by anything the pitch rose higher and higher. The other variation was in the spacing of the grunts or the tempo of the monotonous sounds.

Fortunately for the gorillas, they have very expressive faces and many of their communications involve the raising or lowering of eyelids, the changing position of their lips and how open or shut the mouth is. These facial gestures, combined with the grunting make for a fairly large vocabulary. Body, arm, and leg gestures also help gorillas understand one another. For real threatening gestures the gorilla thumps his chest with both hands. If he is so mad that chest thumping is not enough, he stamps his feet. The gorilla is not always given to such drastic gestures, however. Mbongo could indicate to Ingagi how he was feeling and what he had in mind by the rhythm of his walk, his posture or the way he held his arms.

Such subtlety of gesture is common among animals. A mother monkey may at first have to collar her wandering offspring and toss him onto her back in a long-distance carrying position but within a few months a simple glance from the mother and a slight turning gesture on her part will be enough to bring the youngster scurrying. The scurry ends in a wild leap onto her back—just where she wanted him.

This use of gesture for communication can be observed in domestic pets and farm animals. John Muir's experience in "reading" the signs of oxen is one example. But anyone with a pet and half an ounce of observation can read gestures, too. We have, for example, a black dog and a black cat in our home that have lived together in mutual respect for some time. They are not what you would call bosom friends although there occasionally is a little affectionate head rubbing or ear licking between them. But when cat appears unexpectedly in the kitchen where the dog may be lying, dog always shows interest. Not long ago I noticed that on some encounters, dog rose and playfully chased cat to a table top. On other occasions, dog looked at cat but did not move to chase her. I put this down to dog's laziness. Then I noticed that if cat came into the room with her tail waving high over her head, dog felt free to chase her playfully. But if cat came in with tail lowered, dog never moved. Raised tail indicated, no doubt, that the cat was feeling amiable and was going nowhere in particular. Lowered tail meant "Don't bother me buster, I've got something on my mind."

Gestures, in fact, can be very complex and consist of a lot more than either a tail-up or tail-down attitude. Gibbons who are friends, for example, and meet after some time of separation rush toward each other. If they are brachiating along at top speed through the trees, they slow down as they near one another. Then, hanging by one arm and with legs drawn up, they embrace. Not like two social ladies at a tea party, barely touching each other. But a good, hearty embrace. They reach out with an arm and two legs and hug. They also, according to the sober scientist who observed all this, show a peculiar facial expression. "The corners of the mouth are drawn back, baring the teeth." They smile. Going further, the scientist saw that all the monkeys' motions and gestures in such greeting were relaxed and gentle and that they nearly always give a little cry of welcome. When a gibbon approaches a human with whom he is friendly, the scientist observed that "the animal may protrude its lips, squint its eyes and repeatedly make a soft clucking sound with its mouth closed. Meanwhile it extends its arms and belly for closer contact with the person."

The gestures that communicate anger and antagonism are equally easy to spot. When he is angry, a gibbon opens and closes his mouth rapidly as if snapping his teeth. He moves restlessly with sharp, sudden jerks of arms and legs. If he really is angry, he shakes branches and stamps up and down. Even the most stupid gibbon gets the message. And it is through all these gestures that a lot of gibbon talk is accomplished. It is always accompanied with a great many other gestures of hand-waving, arm-carrying, leg-stance and so on to build a complex vocabulary of meaning for other gibbons in the group.

Elephants have about as limited a speaking vocabulary as the gorillas mentioned above. They can trumpet away all they want to but can't do much for an encore. They can, however, get their messages across through gesture and there is no more expressive baton in the symphony of animals than the curling and uncurling and twisting and swinging trunk of an elephant. His ears, too, tell a great deal. He waves them, moves them forward and outward and altogether, with trumpeting, earwaving and trunk-twisting manages to get along without misunderstanding—at least among other elephants.

Are any animals really deaf and dumb? Yes, quite a few, particularly the least developed animals. Clams, alas, are both deaf and dumb so far as science knows—and so are waterfleas. Countless animal life that low on the scale of complexity have little or no means of audible or gesture communication. But as we climb the ladder of complexity grasshoppers come to light and crickets and cicadas. They make sounds by what science calls stridulation. They rub their wings over their knobby legs and the beat goes on. Some praying mantises make what has been described as a very mournful sound by rubbing their tummies against their wings. Others hiss.

And contrary to a popular delusion most snakes are deaf. This immediately brings to mind the question about the truthfulness of the Hindu fakirs who blow through flutes and get cobras to rise out of baskets. The often filmed scene is more than partly false. It's all false. Not only is the snake deaf but his mouth is sewn shut so he can't bite the flute player.

As for hearing the limited sounds they produce, some lower forms like grasshoppers have eardrums of a very simple sort. They're misplaced though. Through some mixup, their ears are located on their legs.

A number of fish make sounds. Some grind their teeth, grunt or occasionally whistle. Others who have developed a gas bladder can snore, hiss, croon and burp to produce noise. But the question of whether fish hear anything has been argued for a long time. They have sensitive nerve endings near the surfaces of their bodies and do receive vibrations through the water.

On up the ladder of evolution there is the spiny anteater whose sole contribution to the uproar is a hiss when alarmed or angry and a champing sound made with its jaws when it is feeling good. The male Koala bear wails during the mating season and unfortunate bystanders in an area where the male has not located a mate report that he goes on wailing, night after night, in a nervewracking manner. When we get to a certain type of mole we find real originality in the production of sound. The little animal has a long nose that is flexible. It bends its nose around, puts it in its mouth and makes a noise like a duck. No one has yet discovered why it makes a noise like a duck.

There are a few animals that make non-vocal noise although not all such sound has meaning as far as we can tell. The drumming of a snipe, for example, comes from the flutter of extended tailfeathers during flight. The American nighthawk or bullbat as it is called in some areas dives on an enemy on the ground and comes up right in front of its unsuspecting nose. The resulting air pressure produces a sonic boom that frequently scares the wits out of the hostile animal. That's real communication.

Can Animals and Humans Communicate?

For the past few years there has been increasing interest in the problem of communicating with other species of animals that form our natural world. In one sense, we have been doing so for a long time. When a farmer shouts at his horse (if he still has a horse) to "Whoa," the animal has learned that that strange noise means to stop. And, as John Muir said, the oxen on his father's farm learned to understand commands in a number of languages. The amusing thought in this type of communication is that man takes pride in having taught the animals to understand what he means when the astonishing thing is that the animal had the ability to learn it. Such communication is very definitely a one-way street for most people, however, because men in the past at least have not believed that the animal had anything to teach man that was worth learning.

Fortunately this attitude is changing a little. Scientists now are making serious attempts to communicate with other species. It may well be quite helpful to us. If, for example, we had been able to communicate with bats, radar and sonar methods of navigation might have been developed a long time ago. For the bat uses a high frequency sound which he emits to guide him around obstacles on dark nights. The sound goes out from the bat's mouth, strikes objects and echoes back to the bat's ears— and now that we know all about radar anyone might say, "Well of course, that's simple. What's so complicated about that?"

Dolphins made the scene with us some years ago. These harmonious creatures of the sea are now on television, at many grand openings and have several year-round shows going at "oceanaria" in Florida and California where they delight audiences from all over the country.

What the dolphins think of this, is not known precisely but

they do seem to enjoy it. If they don't they're the most good-natured animals in the world for men have taken dolphins, so to speak, to their hearts.

Like the bat, the dolphin uses what we call ultrasonic sound. This simply means the animal can produce and hear sounds beyond the range of the human ear.

In one of his many experiments with dolphins, the authority on dolphinology Dr. John Lilly, was trying to have the animal make a whistle of particular intensity, duration and pitch in order to receive a reward. The dolphin was doing fine and the good doctor was happily throwing a reward fish at the dolphin after each correct whistle. Then he noticed that the dolphin was raising the pitch of his whistle a little each time he was called upon. Now the dolphin makes the whistling sound by pushing air out of his blowhole. Dr. Lilly had noticed that he could see the sides of the blowhole quiver each time the dolphin whistled. Very shortly after the dolphin began to raise the pitch of his whistling, the doctor could no longer hear the sound—and yet the whistles were still coming out since he could still see the blowhole quivering. After whistling twice above the doctor's range of hearing, the dolphin dropped his whistle back to a frequency the man could hear and never went beyond Dr. Lilly's hearing range again. In other words, while the doctor was experimenting on the dolphin, the dolphin was testing the scientist. He found the upper limit of man's hearing.

You might say this took a lot of intelligence and you would be right. The dolphin is one of the most intelligent animals on earth. His brain size is equal to or greater than man's and there are scientists who believe the dolphin to be at least as intelligent as humans. The brain of an adult human weighs about 1450 grams; that of the bottle-nosed dolphin about 1700 grams. It is a complex brain and Dr. Lilly has spent years trying to get in touch with it.

He chose the bottle-nose dolphin for a number of reasons. Since his main interest was, as he puts it, "interspecies communication" he determined on an animal that (a) had a brain large enough and complex enough to be comparable to man's; (b) was of a size comparable to man—an elephant would be hard to manage; (c) had some vocal communication system of its own and could possibly mimic human speech; (d) did not inhabit too alien an environment. He ruled out elephants, giant squid, and whales and settled on the dolphin.

There was one more consideration, one the dolphin easily fulfilled. The animal, whatever it was, ought to be at least not unfriendly toward man. Through history the dolphin has been going more than halfway to make friends with men. They have reportedly guided ships through narrow channels to safe harbors, played and frolicked with people bathing in shallow water and, most important, have never been known to attack a human being even when humans have injured or provoked them.

In a sense, then, men have already communicated with dolphins. The animals have learned signals made by men and have even, by their behavior, managed to get a message or two across to us.

One dolphin, in fact, outwitted the men who were experimenting on her. She had been the subject of experiment for months in a nice pool with plenty to eat and people to play with. When the experimenters were finished, they regretfully took the dolphin back to sea and released her. Some weeks later the men were scanning the waters of the sea for another dolphin when they saw, in shallow water, the thrashing body of a large crippled fish—or so they thought. On approaching it, they discovered it was a dolphin. They promptly netted it and took it back to the station to try to save it. On releasing it in the pool, the injuries vanished and the dolphin leaped happily about swimming as powerfully as any other healthy dolphin. The lady had tricked the men into taking her back.

Dr. Lilly's plan was more ambitious than mere expression of friendship. He wanted to establish actual vocal communication with dolphins. He hoped to be able to teach the dolphins to mimic the human voice.

One of the first major obstacles he had to overcome was the difference in the medium in which men and dolphins live. Our voices and ears evolved in air. We hear and speak best in the atmosphere. Underwater we talk as though we had a mouth full of mush and the sounds we hear when our heads are immersed in the water are distorted and sometimes quite painful on our eardrums. In this problem, the dolphin again appears to be the nearly perfect animal to attempt conversation with. The dolphin can make sounds under water and in the air. It is true and the air sounds are not complex noises but the animal can produce them.

In his laboratory on St. Thomas, in the Virgin Islands, Dr. Lilly installed electronic apparatus and hydrophones to overcome the water-air problem. He also began taping all the dolphin sounds and keeping an ear out, so to speak, for any indication that the dolphin was trying to imitate the sounds of human voices.

There are several things that are quite different about a dolphin voice and a human one. One is the construction of the organs that produce sound. They are not identical by any means in man and dolphin. Another major difference between sounds produced by dolphins and men is that dolphins have a very wide range of frequencies they can produce, that is go from relatively low-pitched sounds that humans can hear to extremely high, supersonic ranges of sound. Their ordinary "speaking" range begins near the upper end of the human range and proceeds on upward out of earshot of us. A third major difference is the speed with which the dolphins produce a sound. They "talk" so fast we would have difficulty understanding them even if they were just saying "Please pass the bread." This difficulty, of course, can be overcome by taping their sounds and slowing them down to hear if they actually are saying anything in ordinary people-talk.

Dr. Lilly got a dolphin and began his experiments. He hooked up hydrophones, microphones and tape machines and his assistants began listening in. For the first few weeks, the dolphin was not really accustomed to his confining, isolating tank. But when he was fully at home, he would whistle and utter creaking noises and he responded to one experiment very quickly. The hyrdophone was hooked up to a pre-taped human voice simply saying "One, two, three, four, five." When the dolphin made a sound of any sort, it activated the tape and the voice counted to five. During the time of counting, the dolphin remained quiet as though listening. When the counting ended, the dolphin made what Dr. Lilly termed an "attention-getting call." Since the animal was isolated and thought he had made a friend through the hydrophone it was only natural to call his new friend over to play.

During the long course of his experiments, the doctor believed he heard the dolphin mimicking the human voice several times. He also noticed a change in the dolphin's noises during its period of isolation from other dolphins. Hearing only human voices, its own "talk" became, as Dr. Lilly put it, like Donald Duck quacking.

So far, however, there has been no real communication on a verbal level with these intelligent animals of the sea. There may be a number of reasons for this. Experimenters may be doing something drastically wrong that makes it impossible to "talk" with dolphins. There's another possibility, though. It may be that even in the brief contact with man the dolphins have made, they have decided more harm than good will come of a closer association. It has yet to enter the head of the scientists that they may have been rejected by a "lower" animal.

Attempts to teach other animals to talk have not produced very interesting results. The birds that imitate the human voice have too limited a brain. Even one of these, a pet crow, may have decided that man doesn't make the best friend in the world. He learned to bark like a dog.

It would seem that some of the higher apes could communicate with man and attempts have been made in this direction—always by trying to get the animal to talk. But their vocal apparatus isn't as flexible as ours and we may have been asking them to do the impossible. One team of researchers is currently getting around the problem. At the University of Nevada, Drs. R. Allen and Beatrice T. Gardner, have been working on a baby chimpanzee. The chimp has never heard the sound of a human voice. Both researchers use the sign language of the deaf when in the chimp's presence. So far as the chimpanzee is concerned, humans don't make noises. At two and a half years of age, the chimpanzee has learned twenty signs including, now, such names of objects as "dog" and "flower." Pretty good for a two-and-a-half year old anybody.

How Dumb Are Dumb Animals?

Men take great pride in having large brains. It is a pity they don't do much more at times than stand around and gloat over it. Lower animals, on the other hand, don't stand around gloating over anything. They are far too busy using their small brains on the thousands of problems that make life interesting for animals with small brains.

One of the continuing problems nearly all animals have is finding enough food to stay alive. If the species is carnivorous and in an area where food is scarce, the carnivorous species may look on any passerby as fair game for the next meal. If the passerby happens to be a man, what's the difference?

Most carnivores have little difficulty in catching a man to eat once they spot him. The fact of man's large brain doesn't make a great deal of difference if the man is unarmed. Under the threat of becoming a meal for some other animal, man usually panics and acts like any other flight animal trying to escape. He often does not make it since he can't run very fast and is not at home in the environment where carnivores lurk. His large brain is no substitute under those circumstances for a gun to shoot with or a fast getaway car.

Such a thing happened to one man in an Antarctic expedition many years ago before helicopters and radio and all man's technology came to the Southern Continent. A member of Sir Ernest Shackleton's ill-fated Trans-Antarctic Expedition of 1914 was floating about in the Antarctic Ocean on an ice field with the rest of the expedition. (Their ship had been crushed in the ice and they were trying to escape to the north and open water.) Ignoring Shackleton's orders and those of his lieutenants, this man wandered away across slushy ice for a short walk. All he could see was gray sky, miles and miles and miles of heaving ice and one lone seal resting on the surface of a floe some hundred yards from the camp.

Being somewhat foolhardy, the man leaped cracks in the ice to other floes and strolled on to have a look at the seal. Ordinary seals are about as harmless as creatures can be, particularly when they are out of water flapping around on the ice. But this was not an ordinary seal. It was a member of a quite aggressive branch of the seal family, called a sea leopard.

To the sea leopard, the man looked like a meal. Instead of retreating as the man approached, the sea leopard waited until the man came quite near and then he attacked. Now the man had heard of sea leopards. But he didn't quite believe the stories he had heard.

The fact that he was being attacked by a sea leopard finally sank into the man's large brain and he turned to run. Now nearly any man can outrun a seal. But in this case there was a serious drawback. The surface of the ice floes was a mass of watery slush. The man's feet sank into it and occasionally he stepped in a really deep pool of water that brought him to a standstill. The sea leopard, meanwhile practically swam through the slush, slithering toward the man much faster than the man could stumble back toward camp. The man leaped across the gaps between floes, shouting to his distant friends as he struggled. The sea leopard got closer to him and it appeared that man would become meal.

At the edge of a floe, the sea leopard plopped into the water and disappeared, briefly. In water his speed increased many times and he swam beneath the ice to the next break where he raised his head above the ice edge directly in the path of the struggling man.

At this point, Shackleton's second in command, Frank Wild, fired a shot from his rifle and ended the sea leopard's career. In recounting his feelings later, the man who had been pursued admitted that he had the odd feeling of being outwitted by an animal. The sea leopard was using his small brain; the man who misjudged the whole situation and nearly lost his life had stopped using his from the moment he left the encampment.

Much more obviously dangerous is another form of sea life, killer whales. These are relatively small whales (twenty to thirty feet long) that are definitely carnivorous. The stomachs of these whales, when they are killed, have yielded the bodies of many seals. They will go after the largest of whales, the blue whale, and get a death grip on the jaws of these largest animals on earth. They hang on until the blue whale tires and then begin eating.

Antarctic veterans of Shackleton's day knew the killer whales were dangerous to men and dogs when they have to cross ice floes. If the killers are around, such crossing of floes is an uneasy business. Both Shackleton and Scott in their early polar expeditions experienced the strange feeling of being regarded as nothing more than a snack by killer whales. Scott at one time was trying to load ship as it lay tied to the edge of ice far out from shore. One of his men named Ponting had tied several sled dogs on the ice and was approaching them when killer whales raised their heads from the nearby water and took a quick look around before submerging. The sight of these large toothed whales so close gave Ponting the shivers but he felt perfectly safe on the ice. Then suddenly the ice erupted beneath his feet and he went sprawling backward. The killers had spotted men and dogs. They sounded and moved up through the water striking the thin ice floe a shattering thwack with their heads. The floe split open and if the dogs had not been tied to the ship, they would have become Jonahs in the whales' bellies. Ponting himself was thrown back to more solid ice but had he been a few feet further out, he might have been eaten.

These whales, indeed all whales, have respectably large brains. They are as keen as that of dolphins (indeed dolphins are warm-blooded mammals and strictly speaking are in the same zoological classification, *cetacean*). The killer whale is no exception. He may, in fact, have a language all his own and ways of passing along information to his fellows very rapidly. A whaleman from a modern whaling fleet that operated in the Southern Ocean recounted a story of killer whales' intelligence that is more than a little startling. Modern whaling fleets have a factory ship that processes the captured whales. All other ships are equipped for the actual hunting of whales. They are small, fast, and have a modern harpoon gun mounted like a cannon on the bow of each one.

It seems that a regular fishing fleet was also in Antarctic waters near the whaling fleet and the ships in this fleet were identical to the hunting ships of the whalers. The fishing fleet had been plagued by a large group of killer whales that had followed the ships and eaten or driven away the fish the men were trying to catch. In desperation, the master of the fishing fleet called for some whalers to come over and drive off the killer whales. So they hurried over, harpoons loaded and ready to go. One shot was fired and a killer whale was hit. All killer whales disappeared immediately, sounding and swimming out of sight. From that moment on the killer whales avoided the hunting ships of the whaling fleet but still harassed the fishing boats when the whalers were not around. And the only difference between fishing and whale hunting ships was the harpoon gun mounted on the bow of the whalers.

You can almost hear the injured whale calling out, "Fellows, stay away from those characters that have the big bump up front. It's bad news, boys. Really bad news." With this the whale expires and a bronze plaque is later installed in the whale hall of fame—next to the one for Moby Dick.

The fact that whales have a vocal method of communicating has only recently been proven. Oceanographers at Woods Hole,

Massachusetts have tape recorded whale talk from deep beneath the sea.

You might argue that whales, like most cetaceans, have quite a large brain—so it isn't surprising that they can do odd, human-like things such as talking. But brown rats have smaller brains and yet they too have a system for communicating bad news. If the leaders of a rat pack come across poisoned food—and the fact is recognized by the experienced leader—he will pass it by. No rat following him will touch the food. In many cases, to insure the health of the pack, the leaders will defecate on the food. But what happens when the leaders die? How does the knowledge get passed on? Scientists do not know precisely but from generation to generation, the word *is* passed along and the pack survives and thrives. If a new poison is invented by men, a few rats will be killed but then the news of that problem is communicated and the poison becomes less effective. Rats are as ingenious as men in this way. And in cities where old buildings are torn down, the swarms of rats that are uncovered provide reasonable proof that we have been living side by side with a very sophisticated animal species. They're smart enough to escape our daily notice and so, you might say, the two species (man and rat) occupy the same territory.

Birds do not have as large or complex a brain as rats. Yet they, too, get along very well. One species in England discovered the delights of fresh milk. Watching from the telephone lines during the early morning hours, they noticed a peculiar human driving along in truck. He would stop at certain doorsteps and leave a glass bottle filled with white liquid. It occurred to one curious bird to examine the situation so he pried the lid off the bottle and drank a little of the stuff. Magnifique! What a taste thrill! Soon the birds were waiting for the milkman and opening all the bottles after he had left. The milk company struck back by replacing the cardboard lids with metal caps. The birds figured those out and managed to twist them off. Within a very short time the news that milk was a tasty, heady beverage had spread among members of the species until they were popping the tops off milk bottles all over Europe.

Well, one says, wasps aren't that bright. They follow instinctive patterns of behavior that are coded in their genes. And they certainly don't have much in the way of brain size. To which insult, the wasps buzz in a loud angry chorus.

Many years ago a diligent researcher worked with wasps in a devilish way. The digger wasp was one species he worked with. This wasp ordinarily tucks its eggs in a hole in the ground, stuffs caterpillars in—enough to see the egg hatched and well-fed when it comes out—and seals the hole with a mud she makes up. And that, according to the computer programmer, is that. There is the end of a chain of events governed by instinctive behavior. The experimenter poked a hole in the lid and watched. The digger wasp wandered around over a number of sealed holes where she had buried eggs and came across the vandalism that had been committed to her nest. With scarcely a pause for thought, she patched the hole with newly made mud.

The point is that patching holes in the lids was not part of her programming.

Another species of wasp provided even more interesting news

for the wasp-watcher. This type makes little marbles of clay, plants an egg in each one, stuffs in morsels like caterpillars for food and seals the little ball of clay up tight.

Evil researcher punched a hole in one and the caterpillars spilled out. Mother wasp stuffed them back in and resealed the pellet—again, this had never happened to her and she was not supposed to know what to do about the emergency.

Then the researcher punched a hole in the pellet that could not be patched from the outside. Caterpillars spilled all over the place as usual and mother wasp came on the scene. Now this type of wasp always builds the clay pellets from the outside. In all the experience she had—or her mother, her grandmother or greatgrandmother—there had never been a need to go inside the pellet to build one or patch one. What to do? The wasp turned the pierced pellet round and round for two hours. Darkness came and mother wasp retired for the night. What a restless night that must have been! Toss and turn, toss and turn.

When daylight came, she hurried to the damaged ball of clay and set to work patching it—from the inside.

CHAPTER VII

You Go Your Way, Charlie, and I'll Go Mine

WE WERE LOST. And we had a fully trained, certified U. S. Air Force navigator on the plane. Let's call him Charlie. He was a captain and had many ribbons on his uniform. How did we get into the mess? Easy.

The flight began in Wales in the British Isles and the first stop had been the Azores. The plane was filled with air and ground crew personnel winging their way homeward at the close of World War II. We made the Azores all right and managed to complete the second leg of the flight without mishap, landing in Gander, Newfoundland. The next morning, so I thought, would see us safely on the ground at Bradley Field, Connecticut but as we headed down the coast, doubts entered my mind. The navigating on the last leg of the journey was being handled by the Captain-Navigator and he was busily trying to tune the radio compass to the Bradley Field station.

Now the radio compass is a simple mechanism. Tune in a station and a needle points to it. Point the plane in the direction of the needle and you arrive over the station. What could be simpler?

But the navigator was having difficulty. He couldn't tune in the Bradley frequency. For some reason, another strong station overrode the signal and the needle wandered aimlessly about in a circle. While the captain in his little cubicle in the nose of the plane swore and fumed, I watched the coastline of Rhode Island and southeastern Connecticut pass beneath the wing. We had planned to stay along the shore until we got to a point south of Bradley Field and then turn inland. Bradley is located above Hartford in the northcentral part of the state not far from the Massachusetts line.

So we winged along waiting for the navigator to tell us when to turn and what heading to take. The needle still wandered aimlessly.

Soon Long Island came into view. We were over Long Island Sound. No word from the navigator. In a very few moments, I reasoned, we would be over New York City so I called the navigator and asked for a bearing. He was still swearing.

Since the Captain-Navigator couldn't find Bradley Field, I switched the radio compass back under my control and began fiddling with it. The strong signal indeed was keeping the needle from coming to rest and I wondered idly where the strong signal came from. From its call letters, I discovered it was from Westover Field just north of Bradley in Massachusetts. Without mentioning it to the navigator, I tuned the radio to Westover and the needle hummed into position like a bird dog pointing. I turned the plane north and flew to Westover. Then, glancing at the map, I turned on a heading that would take us somewhere near our destination. After a few moments, Bradley Field appeared beneath us and I began to let down, preparatory to landing.

It was embarrassing, getting lost on the last and easiest leg of the flight home, and with a Captain-Navigator, too. As we descended, circling the field, I glanced out the window and saw two gulls soaring beside us briefly. One turned his head and peered at me. He turned away toward his companion as if to say, "Look at those bird-brained characters, will you? All that equipment, and they get lost."

The sea gulls disappeared in the distance as we turned down to the landing pattern. They were fifty miles from salt water but I doubt that they were headed in the correct direction to get there. How do birds manage this strange problem of navigation—without benefit of a certified Captain-Navigator? It is a question that has bothered men for years.

Annually, millions of birds migrate over long or medium distances and most of them get where they're going safely. A few species have a peculiar ability to find their way to their nest or home from a long distance away no matter in which direction from the nest they may be taken. This homing instinct is most clearly demonstrated in the famous homing pigeon and men have made use of the instinct by having the birds carry messages to their nests in man-made lofts.

Many years ago before men developed fast means of communication and transportation, his immobility gave him a strange picture of bird life. Robins "appeared" at certain times of the year and "disappeared" at others. Ducks arrived on lakes and ponds—and then flew away. The seasonal changes seemed to have something to do with it, but no one knew quite what. Indeed many years ago a species of bird that hung about the muddy lake shores was believed to bury itself in the mud during the winter. This odd belief sprang from the observed facts:

one day in spring there were no such birds among the bull-
rushes; the next day there were. At the onset of winter they
vanished overnight as mysteriously as they had arrived. It occurred to no one that they had flown away. "Why should they
fly away?" the village sage might have remarked. "This is a
good place to live. I've lived here all my life. And what's good
enough for me is good enough for . . ." So the amusing deduc-
tion was that birds buried themselves in the mud for the winter
months. (No one bothered to test this by digging around in the
mud, but the explanation satisfied everybody so they let the
problem alone. Why stir up trouble—or mud?)

But, as was bound to happen sooner or later, some scientists
asked themselves serious questions about bird navigation and
over the last several decades many of them have conducted
elaborate experiments to discover answers. They tried very hard
to begin with open minds on the subject and all sorts of sug-
gestions were made.

One of the humblest ideas put forward was that migratory
birds guided their flight by simply looking at the familiar landscape. Birds have good vision and their eyes, compared to their
head and brain size, are enormous. But this idea went to pieces
when they considered the known fact that some birds migrate
only during the night hours. It was further shattered when
young birds were taken from their parents before the migratory
season, moved to a distant and strange location and released
after most members of their species had long gone south. Without much hesitation the ignorant youngsters took off and flew
south—over land they had never seen before.

Then it was suggested that the birds navigated by having

some sensitivity to the earth's magnetic field—a kind of built-in compass. No one ever found any part of a bird's brain or nervous system or any other part of its body that seemed to be sensitive to the magnetic field of the earth but to test this idea, scientists placed the birds in a strong, man-made magnetic field to "scramble" his supposed magnetic compass. The birds when released, flew off in the proper direction: southerly in fall, northerly in winter.

Another idea concerned the changing temperatures and thermal radiation from the earth's surface. But this thermal radiation does not change constantly from north to south or south to north. Bodies of water, for example, will radiate more heat than adjacent land during the chilling months of autumn and if that body of water is north of a southbound bird, the bird should, if the theory is correct, turn around and head toward the more intense radiation coming from the body of water. The birds didn't do this.

But, men being men and forever curious, they kept at it. A very complicated theory tried to link bird navigation to the rotation of the earth but it fell apart like all the others. And then a very interesting experiment was performed by Geoffrey Mathews of Cambridge University in England. Mathews at the time was concerned with the question of how homing pigeons home.

The homing pigeon obviously got its name from the highly developed ability to get home to its loft when released many miles from it. Men have even made a sport of competing with pigeons in carefully regulated races. Experienced pigeon racers felt that the experienced birds had some visual means of identifying familiar ground and features and using them as a guide to fly home.

Dr. Mathews of Cambridge had trained some pigeons and was working on a long string of experiments to try to come up with a better answer. He handled the pigeons just as they are handled in races. Early in the morning he placed a number in closed containers, put them in the back seat of his car and drove away from the loft in Cambridge. He always took them north of the university town along the country roads which they could not see and arrived about noon at a spot he had chosen which actually was a bit to the west of north. There he released them, but not all at once like the pigeon racers. One he would hold with its head pointed north, one east, one southwest and so on. At the moment of release he watched them. They all rose fluttering from his hands and turned quickly on a southerly course and disappeared from view in the bright blue sky.

Somehow, when released, the pigeons located the homing direction almost instantly. To try to test the "familiar landscape" theory, Dr. Mathews chose flat open terrain with the least number of trees, hills or, other possible landmarks. The pigeons flew south.

Standing there at noon one day watching one pigeon disappear into the blue, Dr. Mathews realized that they all headed toward the sun. In England, at noon when the sun is highest, if you go toward the sun you are heading south. Do the pigeons follow the sun? He remembered in a flash that on cloudy and overcast days, the pigeons seemed lost. They chose any old direction and flew off, taking a much longer time to get home than on days when the sun was shining.

This thought excited Dr. Mathews until he realized with some disappointment that if the pigeon followed the sun he could never reach the loft. For as the sun passed noon it headed westward and a pigeon following the sun would wind up lost over the Atlantic Ocean and never be heard from again.

Of course it was silly to think that the pigeons could adjust their flight direction to the time of day, noting where the sun was and knowing what time it was and so forth and so on.

It had taken men centuries to learn to navigate by the sun and the stars. The breakthrough came when men developed accurate clocks, called chronometers. These could be taken anywhere in the world and yet register the exact standard of Greenwich time. Knowing the exact time and measuring the sun's position above the horizon helped locate a ship's position east or west of Greenwich, England. Without going into vast detail, this is the scheme. If you know that the sun appears over the eastern horizon on the zero longitudinal line in Greenwich, England at exactly 5:04 A.M. on a certain day of the year and you are at some place where the sun is already up a few degrees above the horizon at that precise Greenwich time, then you must be east of Greenwich. How far east depends on how high the sun is. (Your position north or south of the equator can be figured without reference to a chronometer so long as you can see the sun.)

Dr. Mathews knew all this. He also knew that men are smarter than pigeons. So it simply *couldn't* be true that a dumb pigeon could locate himself by the sun. Besides, a pigeon doesn't have a chronometer. Or so he thought at the time.

To test what seemed to be an insane idea, Dr. Mathews resorted to trickery. He divided his group of homing pigeons into three subgroups. He took them out north of Cambridge a little farther along the same general line he had been on. One group was released just after sunrise, a second control group at the usual noon hour, and the third late in the afternoon.

Zounds! They all headed south. For the morning group, the sun was in the east but they headed south. For the noon group the sun was in the south and they headed south. For the late afternoon group the sun was in the west and they headed south.

They do not follow the sun.

To make matters much worse, Dr. Mathews took his pigeons south of Cambridge and released them. Some took up a southerly course at first. But the great majority turned north and got home in time for tea.

Whatever confusion there was in Dr. Mathews mind, there was very little in the minds of the pigeons.

Now the homing instinct, as it is sometimes called, is very evident in the species of pigeon we have named the homing pigeon. It is also nearly as strong in a sea bird called the Manx Shearwater. It is developed to a lesser degree in other species. But many other bird species have a migrating instinct. North in the spring and south in the fall is their motto. And they go by the millions back and forth across our landscape each year. But in migrating, the birds don't have as complex a problem as in homing. In migrating, the bird has only to decide which way is south in the fall; which way is north in the spring. In a homing bird, the question is double: first it is which way is north, south, east or west? And second, am I north, south, east or west of home?

We don't know, of course, whether these questions occur to the bird. What we are doing is putting the problem in terms of the way men would look at it. And since we know that men are smarter than birds. . . . (But maybe we had better drop that argument.)

But it *would* seem that the problem of the migrating bird is less complex than that of the homing pigeon or the Manx Shearwater.

While Dr. Mathews was taking a late tea back at Cambridge after one of his many homing experiments, another scientist in Wilhelmshaven, Germany, Gustav Kramer was tackling the problem of migrating species of birds. It had long been known that in response to some change in the seasons, that migrating birds in cages showed more restlessness and desire to escape during the migrating season than at other times. So Gustav Kramer went to work. He raised a group of baby starlings and kept them all their growing lives in a cage until they were quite tame. The experimental cage Kramer built for them was circular and the inner surfaces were exactly the same all around the circle. The cage had a perch in the center for the young starlings. And Kramer craftily placed a transparent floor in the cage so he could sneak underneath and observe the birds when they fluttered to the wall trying to get out. As the spring migratory season approached, Kramer took one very tame starling and put him in the cage alone. Then he sat under the cage and observed it. The bird moved repeatedly from the perch to the inner wall of the cage in a northwesterly direction, trying to get out. Now the starling had been taken from the nest as a tiny fledgling and hand-raised by the scientist—so he knew it could not have learned the migratory direction from its parents. From time to time, Kramer rotated the cage to be certain that the bird could not be orienting itself with respect to any little item on the inner surface. Next Kramer placed an opaque strip around the circular cage so the bird could not see anything of the landscape outside. Kramer did leave the top transparent so the bird could see the sky and soak up the sunshine. Still the bird fluttered back and forth from the center perch to the inner wall of the cage on the northwest side.

Then Kramer did a really terrible thing. He cut slits in the opaque sidewall screen, hung movable shutters at the slits on the outside. He bolted mirrors to the shutters. By adjusting the mirrors, Kramer directed sunlight into the cage. But the rays coming from the sun were reflected from the mirrors so the light entered the cage ninety degrees off the true direction of the sunlight.

The starling immediately began to try to get out of the cage from a southwesterly side—ninety degrees away from northwest. The angle between his flight direction and the source of light remained the same.

Do birds use the sun to find direction? From Mathews' and Kramer's independent experiments, the answer would seem to be yes. But the question of where they hide their chronometers had yet to be answered.

Is Your Watch Still Ticking Charles?

Call it by any name you wish (endogenous activity rhythm, if you like), most forms of plant and animal life have a clock going inside them. It doesn't have to be a large clock because even near-microscopic animals and plants seem to have it. Plants blossom, open, and close at regular intervals; animals wake up and go to sleep without being told. Some animals, of course, wake in the evening and run around all night; others wake in the morning and run around all day.

One might say, then, for a day-run-around animal, the morning sun stimulates him and he wakes up and when the sun goes down, he goes to sleep.

But there's more to it than that. Put your day-run-around animal in a darkened cage and keep it dark. At a particular time the animal will get up. He'll run around for his usual length of time and then curl up and go to sleep. He'll go on that way for a long time.

Experiments with deer mice (a night-run-around type) in a nearly completely darkened cage with controlled light, temperature, humidity, etc. showed that at just the same time each evening, deer mouse rose and jumped on a little running wheel (thoughtfully provided) and scurried for a long period of time. Then the mouse ate, wandered about, drove the running wheel occasionally, drank some water, ran some more, went to the bathroom. Then it curled up and went to sleep— on time.

Scientists argued there must be something in its home environment that gets to it, some vibration or electromagnetic radiation or something. But suppose you take a deer mouse, for example, living happily in Atlantic City, New Jersey, put it on a fast jet to California while it is sleeping away the day so that it arrives in the different time belt and in an undeniably new environment by about noon. The mouse sleeps peacefully. When it is sundown in Atlantic City, the mouse wakes up and begins scurrying along on its running wheel, just as before. His diurnal clock, the little unheard, ticking mechanism about which we know very little is still set on East Coast time.

Therefore, Charles, there is nothing about the outside environment that tells the mouse what time it is. Of course if you leave the mouse in Los Angeles, he eventually adjusts to that place. His time mechanism shifts and after awhile he's running on West Coast time.

Suppose a homing pigeon has such a clock—chronometer. He's brought up in a particular loft and his clock is set on that time. Suppose he knows where the sun is at any particular time on his clock. Suppose you take him away from that spot so the sun isn't where it should be at a particular time on his clock. Why the poor bird would feel restless. He might want to put the sun where it should be with reference to his particular clock. So he does. He goes home.

Homing birds and migrating birds can orient themselves by reference to their own internal clock and the sun. When the sky is overcast there is trouble in bird-world. And at night. . . . There are birds that migrate only at night. Then there are only stars. No one in his right mind is going to assume that birds can navigate by the stars.

Only Dr. Mathews and a few other scientists. He conducted

some interesting experiments with mallard ducks. He took four groups of them during a spring migratory season. One group he adjusted so its clocks were running six hours behind schedule. A second group he left alone. A third group had its clocks set six hours ahead of schedule. The fourth group was put twelve hours out. Dr. Mathews adjusted the clocks cunningly by putting the birds in artificial environments and gradually shifting the apparent position of the sun at different times of the day—giving them different night and day sequences. Like the Atlantic City deer mouse in Los Angeles, they got used to it.

Then Dr. Mathews released the ducks, all at once. The second group went where it was supposed to go: northwesterly for the spring migration. One group headed southwesterly, another northeasterly (these were the six-hour change groups). The twelve-hour group went in a southeasterly direction, just opposite from the true direction of migration.

Dr. Mathews next adjusted the clocks on four more groups of mallards. This time he released them at night. No problem at all. Each group headed in a northwesterly direction as it should. Star mapping? Preposterous!

Look back a moment at the Captain-Navigator in the homely example at the beginning of this chapter. Thousands of dollars had been spent training the men in the use of the latest navigating equipment of that day. He had even been trained to use a chronometer and sextant to navigate by the position of the sun, though I shudder to think of relying on his observations over the trackless waters of the cold north Atlantic on that homeward flight.

The radio compass and several other radio-positioning devices were at his disposal. And he was really locked in on them. He fiddled with that radio compass as we flew and flew westward along the shore. If he could *only* tune in Bradley Field! The compass was *supposed* to work. It *had* to work.

But don't for heaven's sake, Charlie, look out the window and see if you can recognize the landscape. Don't even glance at the magnetic compass and your map. Remember, Charlie, we live in a scientific age, the pinnacle of man's development. We have the best equipment men can devise using the good old tried and true scientific method. Don't even *think* there might be a flaw in our use of the scientific method. After all, it came out of men's brains and we all know that men's brains. . . . Look, Charlie, if you so much as *doubt* our method in this scientific age, you're guilty of heresy. Think about that, Charlie.

CHAPTER VIII

Who Killed The Guppies?

IT HAPPENS over and over and over again.

The family decides it would be nice to have an aquarium. Father doesn't care for cats. Mother can't stand dogs. Birds make a lot of noise. But fish! Besides it will be educational for the children.

Visits are made; handbooks studied. Father, a center of ignorance on the subject, is consulted by mother and children. And at last the aquarium is in place. Fish are purchased and the ride home changes from excitement to concern as water slops around in the back seat of the car where the children are fighting to be allowed to hold the container. But it's home at last and the nature-loving family hovers about the aquarium as the fish are carefully allowed to enter their new home.

Look at them go!

After an hour of watching them go, family dines, congratulates itself on solving the pet problem and finally it's lights out.

Next morning all the fish but one are dead.

Lamentations.

More fish are bought, but murder strikes again in the aquarium. Each time the murderer swims in lonely grandeur, looking quite healthy.

Father is advised to get a pair of fish that are already married—only a pair. Then when the fish have little fish all will be well. They will all be of the same species so they won't fight. Soon father fish has killed mother fish and all the eggs have disappeared.

And soon the family is sick and tired of murderous fish. The aquarium is no more.

Father ponders the law of tooth and claw and the one about survival of the fittest.

Mother shudders, and thanks heaven she is a civilized human being and that she is protected from all the ravening beasts.

The children are given a good lesson in the evident superiority of people over lower animals. Mary mourns the fish and feels sorry for them. Johnny shrugs, takes up his abandoned six-shooter and returns to the important business of killing Indians—dozens of which have crept up on the house while he was busy with the fish.

It is not only mother and father and Mary and Johnny who have been led to believe that the fish were nothing but cannibals. Trained scientists have been, too. Those interested in studying the behavior of fish have gone through similar experiences. An aquarium is built. Rare species imported. More dead fish.

These are the same people who watched the film and did not question the tiger fight that was staged for them. Even Konrad Lorenz has been fooled by the problem of dead fish. His studies, however, on the instinct of aggression and on territory showed him the way out of the dilemma. He reasoned that the aquarium was too small to allow the natural territory-seeking fish to find and hold enough space to suit them. Observing a group of fish in the small aquarium he saw that one soon occupied the most territory. The others were driven to the far corners of the aquarium where they hid behind the air hose or lurked in the weeds, scarcely ever daring to come out. As time went on, the dominant fish got fatter and more chipper. His colors glowed with health. The others became thin and dispirited and finally turned up their tummies and died, floating on the surface. Even a pair of fish in an aquarium by themselves spelled trouble. The male killed the female.

This came about, Lorenz reasoned, because the fish had no one to fight but each other and the stronger male won. The usual ritualized fighting disappeared in the confined space and deadly combat took its place.

Lorenz solved the problem by getting two pairs of fish, placing them in the small aquarium and separating them with a glass partition. He had defined their territory for them and each time one pair of fish wanted to have a scrap, they rushed at the partition and banged their noses against the glass, glowering at the other pair until their aggression had been worked off. Harmony existed in that aquarium.

But only recently has such understanding of fish and other animal problems been attained. For years, trained observers took animals from the wild and dangerous jungle and put them in cages for observation. Sometimes the cages were imitation jungles. Trees and rocks, with caves in the rocks for the animals to sleep in.

Of course the observers didn't put any of the animal's natural prey in the cage live for the animal to stalk, catch and eat. That would have been cruel. Instead a keeper came around regularly and dumped the food over the wall.

All the time the scientists were observing and making notes about the animal's behavior. Then they wrote papers on the subject and had them published.

The animals grew bored. They scratched themselves and yawned. (Make a note of that: eighth time since sunup that that monkey alone in his cage has yawned.) And finally the monkey turned away and sat sulking in the corner of the cage, his face to the wall. No excitement, no one to fight with. No tails to pull. What's the use?

(Make a note of that: monkey stays all day with face to wall.)

Monkey sickens and dies.

Trained observer calls for an autopsy to see what killed it. It does not occur to him that he killed the monkey.

Fortunately the situation is changing—but only a little. Even in the wild, where observers are going now to do their observing they take a strange, hidden, secret device with them. They don't, in fact, know they have it with them. It's a MEVN. A MEVN is a Man's Eye View of Nature. However well trained the observer may be, he carries this distorting lens with him and only the very best observers escape the distortion when they are at work. It can be argued, in fact, that no human observer can escape looking through that distorting lens all the time and under every circumstance. Not that the scientists are unaware of the problem, or at least some of them.

WHO KILLED THE GUPPIES?

In a recently published paper on animal behavior, Dr. David Rioch of the Division of Neuropsychiatry at Walter Reed Institute of Research warned that "The application of social concepts . . . to the jungle still determines the thinking of considerable sections of our professional population. Many students of human behavior are convinced that the 'law of the jungle' is one of arbitrary murderous threat and attack and that the 'normal' behavior of animals in 'the wild' provides an 'explanation' for the more distorted aspects of human mores. Once the chimpanzee and gorilla had been labelled dangerous, it was virtually guaranteed that methods for killing the adults and capturing the young would be greatly improved, but that it would take years to find out that these animals were responding to the form of the human approach and were not driven by some immutable force to attack and destroy."

In other words, the humans, including the jungle-roaming scientists, were committing the biggest anthropomorphizing blooper of all time. They "attributed the human quality" of murder and indiscriminate killing of all forms of life to the jungle animals. Their thinking went something like this: man is a murderer; therefore all animals must be murderers.

Obviously something was wrong with the thinking process. Or perhaps it wasn't so obvious. But today there is a glimmer of recognition of the problem. Intensive psychological studies on human behavior are dredging up some of the mud from our minds and hearts. It is not, as the writer Alex Comfort says, an optimistic picture. Most men if asked today would give the standard answer to the question: what are the distinctions between humans and animals? Standard answer: the good, the high, the pure, pure Emersonian thoughts and acts are human; all that is base and evil is animal.

"Without any cynicism," Alex Comfort writes, "there is some ground now for reversing the attribution, or at least expanding it. Self-destructive trends are rare in animals, except where functionally built-in; major intra-specific aggression (here he uses 'aggression' in the 'intent to injure' sense i.e. murder) and predation are rarer and become rarest in social species and in the higher primates—no animal fights as Man does, and the general pitch of potential and actual self-destructive behavior which he reaches is quite unique in phylogeny. . . . On the other hand rudimentary society and mutual aid are relatively common in lower animals, both as programmed instinctual activities, and apparently in close correlation with intelligent behavior. Our capacity for love and sociality, as well as our more advertised 'moral sense' are in direct continuity with this part of our animal inheritance."

In other words, man, you just flunked the question. Got it completely hind end foremost. Why? Because of MEVN. That's why.

Well, what is MEVN, anyway? In a very simplified way it is the idea that man is the center of the universe. And the history of that unhappy-making idea goes back over the horizon of western man's beginnings. One of the chief spokesmen for it was that well-known expert, Aristotle. He gave the idea a big push toward popularity when he described the universe for everyone. The earth is at the center of the universe. (It has to be, because we're on it.) The sun, moon and stars all revolve around us. And so on—nearly everyone knows the rest of that description.

And where did good old Aristotle get the idea? Out of his head, naturally, where all good things come from.

Then 2000 years later when Copernicus shot that idea down in flames everybody began to feel sorry for themselves—and they've been pretty distressed about it ever since. To make up for not being at the center of the universe, we have, in the last few hundred years, comforted ourselves with the thought that we're brighter than any other creature. And better. Not like the other animals.

And the other animals and things? Well they're here just especially for us. There they are, waiting. All those goodies.

So, within the short time span of less than two hundred years, the American delegation of western man raped an entire continent.

Man killed off the bison, the carrier pigeon, and several other species of animals. He would have exterminated egrets, musk-oxen, fur seals had he not been stopped by a few panicky conservationists. He would have turned the entire midwest into a dustbowl had not the first hint of what he was doing hit him where it hurt—in the pocketbook. The wornout, red clay land of the south and the cutover land of the north are still with us despite "Soil Banks" and other reclamation measures.

Not being allowed to wear out any more land, we're trying to:

Flood the Grand Canyon by building a dam to generate electric power to operate our electric toothbrushes.

Chop down all the redwood trees possible (the largest living plants) before a group of panicky conservationists stakes out a sufficiently large stand of the trees to allow them to survive.

Kill off the largest animal the world has ever seen—the blue whale.

Foul the atmosphere of the entire planet with the burning of fuels and radioactive fallout.

Oh, and we are polluting the water too, in all our streams and rivers.

And the ocean! What an opportunity! We can dump our sewage there, sink all the radioactive wastes to the bottom. (Never mind what it does to the fish.) Indeed yes, the ocean offers itself as the largest goodie of all. And the last one.

This is MEVN. Hard at work.

". . . no creature other than man has ever managed to foul its nest in such short order." So writes Dr. Lynn White Jr. in a recent issue of *Science*.

And speaking of science, why doesn't science do something about all this? It is a little difficult to get science, or its large mongoloid companion, technology to *do* anything. They simply *are*. Men do the doing. Both science and technology are still somewhat directed by men and there are at least two powerful reasons why men cannot "fix things."

The first is that these same men in their pursuit of progress, employing the enlightened advances of science and technology are the ones who caused the situation. Behind the men on the frontiers of progressive science stand rank on rank of enlightened executives in the Federal Government and all the large corporations of the land. Back of them, of course, stand the unaware people panting for the latest item of convenience.

In a new college textbook edited and written by Harvard and Yale historians, there is an interesting sentence that makes you wonder whether men in fact *can* control the twentieth century progress-monster they have created. It reads "Technology, capital, productivity, and marketing, with all that they involve, determine to a large extent how we live."

It is often popular to become angry with "where science is taking us." And usually the solution offered is a kind of "back to nature movement." But western man can't "get back to nature" in any way at all because he is still blocked by MEVN. Science didn't start MEVN nor did technology. Aristotle didn't either.

MEVN is peculiar to western religion. It is part and parcel of the very beginnings of our religious heritage and even people who claim no longer to believe that heritage are influenced by it in many subtle ways.

Dr. Lynn White Jr., mentioned above has stated the problem in his *Science* article with a great deal of force.

He writes "Especially in its Western form, Christianity is the most anthropocentric (man-centered) religion the world has seen. As early as the 2nd century both Tertullian and Saint Irenaeus of Lyons were insisting that when God shaped Adam he was foreshadowing the image of the incarnate Christ, the Second Adam. Man shares, in great measure, God's transcendence of nature. Christianity in absolute contrast to ancient paganism and Asia's religions . . . not only established a dualism of man and nature but also insisted that it is God's will that man exploit nature for his proper ends."

Dr. White then points out that in pagan religions the idea of spirit in nature was a central one. Trees, rocks, animals, the earth itself, contained different spirits and then he writes "By destroying pagan animism, Christianity made it possible to exploit nature in a mood of indifference to the feelings of natural objects."

And there you have it. The very beginning of MEVN. All the scientists, all the technologists who have contributed to the rise of western power have been peering through the invisible but important lens of MEVN.

Even when men are aware of the problem, they find it almost impossible to escape from MEVN. In their writing, a word or a phrase gives them away. Take for example the thoughts of Dr. René Dubos, professor of environmental biomedicine at Rockefeller University. In lecturing on the subject "Science and Human Affairs" Dr. Dubos speaks of a possibly worthwhile goal of "Manipulating the environment in such a manner that it evolves in harmonious relationships with human beings." There's MEVN at work and making the thought come out backward. What about "Manipulating human beings in such a manner that they evolve in harmonious relationship with the environment?"

Even Dr. Lilly, with his great feeling for the dolphins with whom he experimented for so long, has a bit of MEVN at work. In fact, trying to *avoid* it, he falls under its influence twice in a single sentence. Sentence: "These animals (dolphins) have large and fine brains and this fact should make us pause before we attempt to treat them the way we have treated other animals with less to offer us."

Here they are:

1) Dolphins have big brains, as we do, and this is the standard of our worth or non-worth that should be applied in deciding how to treat the creature.

2) The last four words of the sentence: less to offer us, imply that all animals exist for our purposes and should be rated as good or bad, useful or not useful, only in terms of what they can do for us.

Once you get onto the trick, you find MEVN statements all around. Take this famous line of poetry from Gray's *Elegy in a Country Churchyard*

"Full many a flower is born to blush unseen,
And waste its sweetness on the desert air."

What does he mean "waste?" Meaning: Because a human isn't there to sniff the flower, the flower is wasting its life away. And what about "blush unseen"?

Of course the obvious phrases come to mind. "Man conquers nature" is a favorite and "battling the forces of nature" usually turns up in news reports of "disasters" involving high winds and high tides. And curiously it is only during those "disasters," that men are stripped of MEVN completely. They then battle for their lives as do all other creatures caught in some momentary convulsion of their global home.

The Guppies Fight Back

Coupled to the delusion of MEVN is an abysmal human

ignorance of nature as shown by Mother, Daddy, Mary, and Johnny with the guppies. Of course such ignorance is not confined to them for, until very recently, the scientists were nearly as ignorant. But as ignorance of the law is no excuse in court, so ignorance of the natural law is none in the world.

This state of ignorance is clearly shown in Dr. Rioch's statement about chimpanzees and gorillas "responding to the form of the human approach."

Assume for a moment, a happy family of chimpanzees at home. Things are going well on a particular day and then, quite without warning, the chimpanzees find themselves surrounded by strange creatures. The creatures close in on them making loud noises. Several adults are killed; others have long vines tied to them and are hauled away. And in a moment what had been a happy chimpanzee family is no more. One of the captured chimpanzees manages to bite one of the creatures—who immediately calls for iodine and is outraged that the chimpanzee bit him.

Critical distance has been mentioned before. It is that least distance you can be from a wild, cornered animal before the animal attacks and is literally fighting for its life. It is the most serious combat known to the animal world and when such a fight begins, the animal, whatever it is, will use all of its strength, all of its weapons, all of its skill and intelligence to preserve its life. But ignorant of this, many people approach animals in the zoo or in the open if they come across them with the peculiar idea that since they are men the animal will not dare bite them.

From time to time, newspapers report the sad incident of

the child or adult who reached through the bars of a cage to pet the dear little ocelot or raccoon and found that the animal did not interpret the gesture as one of affection. Stunned relatives quickly demand the execution of the vicious animal that had the nerve to bite Jimmy or Mabel.

In the wild, the method of self-preservation used most often by animals against man, is flight. The deer, the bear and all the animals know an enemy when they smell one. And to many animals, man smells pretty bad. Man, with his stunted sense of smell, does not realize that smell is a very important dimension in the lives of many animals. And the peculiar odor of the human body carries far on the winds so that animals such as bears, can escape even being seen by most people who go out into the wilderness areas.

But the struggle of most species of animals to stay alive with the human onslaught continuing is a losing one. With weapons, with nets, with thoughtless destruction of the environment, we are each year killing off more and more of vanishing species—along with guppies.

Is Man the Only Immoral Animal?

Albert Schweitzer and St. Francis of Assisi were two men brought up in the western tradition. They were believers in Christianity as well as the highest moral principles developed over the centuries of western civilization. Yet these two men are almost the only well-known examples of men who saw the need for a moral outlook on all of life, not just human life.

Modern and ancient codes of ethics and morality concern themselves solely with man's relation to man. Schweitzer and

St. Francis concerned themselves with man's relation to the living world. They were thought by many people to be more than a little bit odd. They were not practical in the usual western sense. Their concern with nature was believed to be sentimental or vaguely romantic, like that of Rousseau's enchantment with nature. Yet looking at the recent studies of psychologists reported by Alex Comfort, you could argue that only when man discovers his true position in the natural scheme of things, only when he recognizes himself as a part of nature (rather than apart from nature) can he begin to become a moral animal.

Even among people today who are not in sympathy with the ideas of St. Francis or Schweitzer, there is growing concern that man, the animal, is a species headed for extinction—not to mention the extinction of other forms of life we could destroy in the process. The extinction of a species because of its failure to develop self-preserving physical and behavioral characteristics is nothing new.

In fact there are two species of birds right now heading into a blind alley of evolution. The Argus pheasant and the peacock both have problems. In selecting males for pairing and mating, the females of both species are most interested in the size of display feathers, on the male. In the case of the Argus pheasant these are wing feathers, in the peacock, the tail feathers. This means that more chicks of each species will be produced by the males having extraordinarily large wing or tail feathers—so large the birds are unable or nearly unable to fly. And if they cannot fly they cannot escape their natural enemies who prey on them for food. Result: exit Argus pheasant and peacock.

Some scientists believe today that man is in the same boat with the Argus pheasant and the peacock. As Konrad Lorenz writes, "The rushed existence into which industrialized, commercialized man has precipitated himself is actually a good example of an inexpedient development caused entirely by competition between members of the same species." And he goes on to say that, so far as he can see, western man has as little hope of changing directions at this point as the Argus pheasant.

Not that some attempts are not being made. In 1963, scientists from many fields of study—zoology, psychology, psychiatry, biology, anthropology, ethnology and others—met in London for a joint discussion of man's aggressive instinct or behavior. The title of the resulting papers that were gathered in book form was *The Natural History of Aggression*. The papers presented ranged from "Aggression in Social Insects" to "Possible Substitutes for War."

In 1967 in Washington, D. C. the American Anthropological Society held its annual meeting. The topic: *War, The Anthropology of Armed Conflict and Aggression*. One of the papers by Margaret Mead ended with the sentence "Our knowledge of biological behavior of all sorts, and particularly human behavior is so imperfect that long term planning without allowance for multiple feed-back often does more harm than good."

And that is about as far as we have progressed in solving our problem.

Even a casual glance at mankind, particularly western mankind, shows some fairly upsetting things to be true.

Man is an aggressive animal, however you define the term.

Man has a territorial instinct.

Many animals share these same instincts but manage their affairs much better than we do.

Man is the only species that condones the killing of its own species.

So far, man has done little or nothing to examine himself and change his blind, suicidal course.

It is not the aim here to pinpoint the thousands of as yet unknown causes of war. But we don't have to go to the international front to find "war" that shows off mankind as an irrational creature. You can look around you, in any large city today to find a good example.

CHAPTER IX

Hey Man! Shape Up or Ship Out

THE EIGHTEEN BOYS in the candy store on that hot night in July were certain of one thing: before the night was over, somebody was going to get messed up. All were members of a juvenile gang called the Egyptian Kings in New York City. Eleven were under fifteen years of age; the other seven were between fifteen and eighteen.

They had grown up together in the same city neighborhood —a neighborhood of old apartment houses, untidy streets, candy stores and drug stores, poolrooms and bars and delicatessens. The gang was formed, they said, to protect the smaller kids in their neighborhood from being beaten up by members of a rival gang farther uptown called the Jesters.

From time to time, the Jesters—two or three at a time— would invade the neighborhood of the Egyptian Kings, find a boy younger and smaller than themselves and beat him up. They would rob him and head back to their own neighborhood.

To take revenge, members of the Egyptian Kings would sometimes invade the Jester's neighborhood and do the same thing. Neither of the rival gangs went into the other's territory except on the sneak raids—with only one exception.

A public swimming pool was located in Jester territory and sometimes a number of the Kings would go up there for a swim. The pool, according to city law, was open to any citizen no matter where he lived or who he was. But the Jesters and the Kings obviously did not live by the laws of the city.

On one occasion several Kings went up to the pool and while they were standing around, a group of Jesters closed in on them. The Jester leader pulled out a forty-five calibre pistol and held it against the back of an Egyptian King. Another Jester waved a sawed-off rifle. The Kings dived into the pool where they were in effect held prisoners by the encircling Jesters.

Finally the Kings managed to persuade several smaller boys to sneak out of the pool and go for help. When the reinforcements arrived, the water-logged Egyptian Kings made their escape.

As the days of the hot summer passed, the Kings stayed away from the pool. But they did not forget the humiliation of the incident. In fact, as they talked about it among themselves, they got angrier with each passing week. Finally they decided that nothing would restore their honor but a full scale rumble.

Their leader sent word to all members of the gang; he called on leaders of friendly gangs in other parts of the city. The Kings met on street corners or in candy stores and discussed the coming fight. They also told one another what they had overheard about the Jester's battle plans. There were many rumors, among them that knives and guns and chains would be used; that the Jesters would have several hundred members to throw into the battle and drive out the invaders. It was also rumored that the police knew of the coming fight—and to the Kings, the police were another enemy force to worry about.

The day and the time had been set, a day late in July. At eight o'clock in the evening the Egyptian Kings were to gather at a favorite hangout, a candy store above 150th St. When the time arrived, some seventy boys crowded into the store. They were excited, nervous, and frightened—but determined to fight. As they bragged of what they were going to do, their fright lessened; they found strength in the crowd that they formed.

Minutes of waiting passed. Their leader was busy phoning his "allies." The minutes stretched into an hour. The boys had bragged as much as they could and their excitement had reached a climax. It began to disappear. Some of them left the store and walked homeward in the evening light. For a while it seemed that the invasion would not take place, that the rumble was off. The group got smaller as more boys left. Then word came on the phone that the allies they expected would not be able to help them that evening. At last there were only eighteen boys left, but they were determined to go ahead.

The leader gave the word and they set out, in twos or threes, to slip into enemy territory. The meeting point was a small city park near the swimming pool. When the gang assembled there, they sent out two members to locate the Jesters. The rest waited in the shadows. All were tense and excited. As the shadows deepened, everything that moved became, to them, a member of the enemy gang, a Jester. The rustle of leaves, the scrape of a footstep *had* to be a sound from some of them approaching. After only a few minutes of waiting the gang

147

was so tense they were ready to attack anyone who came along.

What came along were two small boys, fifteen years old. They were walking through the park on their way home. One was a cripple, so they walked slowly.

The group of Kings saw the two boys and saw also that they were alone. To them they were unwary Jesters, two of the enemy to be cut down by superior numbers. The Kings moved out of their hiding place and surrounded the two boys.

They attacked the crippled boy first. A fist flew out and hit him in the face. A baseball bat smashed against his head and sent him to the ground. He lay there looking up at the Kings surrounding him. They began to kick him and he warded off the kicks with his hands. Then someone pulled a long bread knife from a paper sack and stabbed the crippled boy in the back.

When the Kings closed in, the crippled boy's friend tried to run. He managed to struggle from the hands holding him and run a few steps. He screamed for his friend to run, too. But several of the Kings caught the boy and threw him to the ground. Then they began to work on him—with fists, feet, clubs, and knives.

As police later tried to learn exactly what happened, they got some description of the fight from the Kings themselves.

"I was watching him," one said, "I didn't wanna hit him at first. Then I kicked him twice. He was layin' on the ground lookin' up at us. I kicked him in the jaw, or some place, then I kicked him in the stomach. That was the least I could do, kick him."

"I was aiming to hit him," another said, "but didn't get a

chance. There were so many guys on him. I got scared when I saw the knife go into the guy. . . ."

"He was down on the ground," a third reported, "Everybody was kicking him, stomping him, punching him and stabbing him so he tried to get up and I knocked him down again."

Another: "The guy that stabbed him . . . he told me that when he took the knife out of his back he said 'Thank you.' "

As suddenly as the fight began, it stopped. The Kings, frightened by what they had done, left their two victims and ran away. All but one. He stayed behind and began swinging at the second boy with a machete. The other Kings called to him. "Come on," they said, "we got him. We messed him up already. Come on."

The gang member with the machete followed the others as they ran away toward their own neighborhood.

The boy who had tried to run could run no longer. He had been beaten and stabbed to the edge of unconsciousness. But he managed to drag himself to a street corner where he was taken to a hospital. His friend, the crippled boy, couldn't make it. He was dead.

Much later, the father of the dead boy said, among other things: "They are monsters—in my mind I classify them as savage animals. . . . This is pure jungle activity."

The eighteen youths of the gang called the Egyptian Kings might be called monsters. That can be argued. What cannot be argued are the other two remarks of the outraged father. As you know, the Egyptian Kings did *not* act like savage animals nor was their murderous fight an example of jungle activity.

Many reasons have been given for gang activity like that described above. Lack of good home training. Poor environment. Frustration with poverty. General decay of morals. No respect for law and order. The list could be continued indefinitely.

Neither the Kings nor the Jesters had ever heard of animals defending a territory nor had they wondered about the instinct of aggression. But both of those things were at work in the fight that ended in murder. And murder, peculiar to man, has been man's problem for as long as we know anything about man or man-like creatures. The Biblical account of Cain's slaying Abel has come down in our heritage as being tragically true. But the greater tragedy is that all men who condemn the murder of fellow men are themselves equally capable of committing murder.

Until recently, the question of why men kill their fellow man, has not found even a partial answer among scientists. From all observation of jungle animals, they have learned of the inhibiting forces at work to prevent murder (the threat gesture, the ritualized fight, the appeasement gesture and the inhibiting mechanism that stops the victor from killing).

In only one species of animal, other than man, has the ability to murder been witnessed. This is among rats. Rat colonies are pretty highly organized societies and members of the same tribe never harm each other. They, in fact, show what we might call a good deal of affection for each other. But if one tribe of rats comes across another tribe, murder can follow— particularly if both tribes are in an enclosed space. The rats distinguish between their tribal and the nontribal members on the basis of smell. A "foreign" tribe smells differently and the rats are roused to such a fury that they slaughter one another until both tribes are nearly wiped out. Gone are the inhibitions, the ritualized fighting. The insane anger they experience rouses them to such a pitch that they will attack members of their own tribe briefly. But on recognizing one another will break off their fight and search for a "foreigner" to kill.

In the murder committed by the Kings the police and sociologists could tell by their questioning of the boys that they were behaving as insanely as the rats. Their behavior climaxed a long list of "little causes." There was the humiliation of the swimming pool encounter. The long-nursed grudge through the summer weeks. The bragging, courage—rousing statements among themselves and, when they actually invaded the enemy territory, the fear—both of the Jesters and of fear itself: the fear they might not be seen as courageous by their fellows.

Murder resulted. In both rat tribes and this human example great controlling emotions took charge—in the one case over instinctual behavior among the rats, in the other over all moral precepts man has tried to learn and live by.

Again, turning to the ethologists' studies of animal behavior, we see that strong inhibiting factors against murder are most strongly at work in carnivorous animals. These animals, such as tigers and wolves, are equipped with deadly weapons to catch and kill their food. And it is just these animals that need the powerful inhibition against murder. The "flight" animals like deer and antelope, fight but they fight in a highly ritualized pattern. The loser ends the fight by withdrawing from the head-wrestling and running away. Carnivores fight according to ritual also but they are fighting with their deadly weapons and it is the appeasement gesture that ends the fight, that brings into play the inhibiting force in the victor that prevents murder.

Where does man fit in?

Man is not carnivorous. Anthropologists, in struggling to roll back the curtain of pre-history and discover who and what man was, are in agreement that from what we know now of man's origins, he was a primate—a berry eating, leaf chewing primate. He then evolved on the ground. For some reason he left the forests and went out onto the grasslands and began to hunt for meat. He became omniverous.

His inheritance from the forest was that of a herbivore and he, like the other primates, probably fought ritual battles and then ran away just as chimpanzees and gorillas do today. Man's background then *did not* produce a murder-inhibiting mechanism like that developed in the wolf and the tiger.

When man left the forests to hunt for meat he had little equipment except his brain. Most large ground animals could outrun him and he had no tooth or claw with which to capture and kill prey in a single leap or with a single blow. So he developed weapons. A stick became a club, a stone became an axe. And he used his brain to work with members of his group in hunting to outwit and trap larger, swifter animals. It all looks so very progressive. But with the stone axe, with the club, man did have the means to kill at a single blow. He became in effect a predator but without the predator's instinct against murdering one of his own kind. He was like a harmless, flighty sparrow suddenly and murderously equipped with the beak and talons of a hawk.

One of the oldest fossils of man yet discovered is a skull of a *Homo habilis,* a very man-like creature in many ways that lived two million years ago. Discovered by Louis Leakey whose work in Tanganyika's Olduvai Gorge has been filmed and photographed widely, the skull was that of a twelve-year old. On the top of that skull is a fracture that had caused its death. It is more than probable that the child was murdered. Man's killing of man goes back a long way; he did not learn to murder yesterday.

Primitive Tribes

The number of primitive tribes in the world today is being reduced as modern technology and tools and all the baggage of civilization reaches further into jungle and mountainous areas. There are some, however, that offer a glimpse of man as he lived, probably everywhere, in the distant past. Almost without exception the primitive tribes being studied in the Western Pacific and Africa and South America are carrying on a running fight with their neighboring enemies. Unlike the fights of the langurs or the callicebus monkeys, the tribes of humans defending a territory, kill one another and, in some few cases, eat their victims.

One primitive tribe, the Yanomamö, is situated in southern Venezuela and northern Brazil. An estimated 10,000 of these Indians live in more than 100 villages, each of which has between forty and 250 inhabitants. Dr. N. A. Chagnon of the

University of Michigan has been studying the Yanomamö for some time. (The first outside contact was made with these Indians in 1950.) The villages form the basic social unit and these villages are constantly at war with one another. Indeed, chronic warfare, according to Dr. Chagnon, is the rule. Not only does village fight village, but there is also a great deal of fighting among men of the same village.

By both breeding and training Yanomamö males are aggressive.

Young boys, as young as four years of age, learn to strike adults whenever they are unhappy about something. The adults give the young males approval by laughing and applauding such behavior. This developing fierceness is needed, or believed to be needed, in the constant warfare between villages. As the young males grow, there are fights among themselves to develop their strength but, more importantly, to develop their will to fight and to kill. There are ritual club fights among the men, a great deal of threatening and shouting (display behavior); weaker members of the village are pushed around and women frequently beaten for real or imagined wrongs. All of this is supposed to develop the supreme virtue of fighting ability.

Indeed the larger villages fight so much within the village that when the number of villagers gets much over 250, the village will split and form two villages. Weaker, smaller villages move about the jungle territory often to find a place where they will not be wiped out by stronger, larger, villages.

In many of their customs, the Yanomamö are like all primitive tribes living in a hostile environment—hostile because of marauding people, not other animals. Through all recorded history during which humans fought to conquer or kill one another, the aggressive instinct has served its primary purpose of group survival but always at the expense of some other group.

The function of the aggressive instinct is plain to see in such a situation. It solidifies the group and prepares it to fight an outside enemy. Highest ranking within the group goes to the most aggressive males.

The Egyptian Kings and the Jesters were very much like primitive tribes but they had developed in the busy streets of the world's largest city. They had a territory. They placed high value on aggressive fighting. They feared *not* to be aggressive because they would lose status (ranking order) if they indicated they did not want to fight.

It is all too easy to believe that there is a vast difference between primitive tribes and civilized societies. In fact, there is very little, so far as human behavior is concerned.

We place a high value on strength and forcefulness.

Our "heroes" are sports figures whose skills in the sports arena are witnessed by millions. These sports are forms of ritualized fighting according to rules and we all have a "home" team representing our territory. The territory may be a school or college; it may be a city or region and, in the case of the Olympic Games, our country.

In many parts of the United States, in many schools and sports organizations, aggressiveness is encouraged. The rules of what is called good sportsmanship govern the displays of aggressive behavior on the sports fields. In fact, ritualized combat with weapons of war is a firm part of western history. The tournaments among knights who fought with lance and broadsword and battle axe established superiority among the individual knights and sometimes settled quarrels between neighboring kingdoms without going to an all out war over the matter.

The last remnants of this sport of fighting are found in the dueling that still goes on occasionally in Germany to settle "matters of honor." As a sport, fencing becomes a bout of skill and swiftness with strict rules which are always obeyed.

Aggression Among Men

As you know, aggression is held to be an instinct by many ethologists. It has, according to them, a number of species preserving results.

Other scientists who do not think aggression is an instinct believe it is a result of frustrations and anxieties caused by an animal's environment. If the frustrations and irritations are removed, they reason, aggression will vanish and the problem of man killing man will disappear. A lot of effort is now going into projects that are supposed to reduce irritations that "cause" aggression. But still, small groups of uninformed boys form gangs, directors of welfare projects fight among themselves, wealthy parents quarrel on PTA committees (ladies, too) and the entire human uproar continues.

You do not have to look far to find aggressive behavior in the world today.

Many examples occur in all communities among groups living in poverty neighborhoods. Where the people use aggression constructively, they band together and turn their aggressive energy to rebuilding their territory, turning it into a useful and proud community. In other neighborhoods the aggressive instinct drives some people to throw bricks, set fires and cause riots. In both cases the condition of the neighborhoods roused the aggressive instincts in the people who live there. In the one case aggression is used rationally, in the other, irrationally.

In both cases, however, aggression is at work. And in both cases the people feel a sense of relief and satisfaction when they have discharged their aggressive impulse. In all animals, aggression stimulates. All the senses and the intelligence work at high levels of efficiency. A person enlivened by an aggressive impulse feels "good" and declares that "he could lick the world." In the words of one scientist who has observed animal behavior for many years: "The healthy animal is up and doing." Alone among all animals, man must decide by using his intelligence exactly what he will be up and doing. He can either kill or construct.

One of the best ways man has learned to respond healthfully to his aggressive instinct is by participating in sporting events. A game or contest is invented. Rules are defined and men and women can "fight" among themselves during the game and be as aggressive as they wish—so long as they do not break the rules.

Professional football is probably the most active contact game played in the United States. To some people it appears brutal and many coaches have explained their interest in the game in unmistakable terms: it is the nearest thing to war that society, when not actually at war, permits.

There are many intricate rules that govern the players' aggressive behavior. Not that they are always obeyed. It is impossible for the referees to see everything that goes on in a pro-football game particularly in the crunching contact of linemen when play starts.

Not at all curiously, the players themselves have developed a set of "sub-rules" as they might be called to take care of the in-fighting that goes on. And when fights start on the field (illegal, slugging matches that stop the game and give the spectators a little extra excitement for their money) the chances are good that one of the players has broken a sub-rule devised by the players themselves.

Underlying even the sub-rules is the commandment: thou shalt not maim. If a player tries deliberately to injure another permanently, he becomes known quickly throughout the league as a true-blue dirty player. Such a player is watched carefully and frequently is "taken care of" at some point by his opponents. He leaves, sometimes on a stretcher, and misses several games.

If nothing else, the period of relaxation gives the dirty player time to think and after six or eight months of mental effort it may occur to him that if he wants to continue to play he will have to obey the rules. So even here in aggression, in ritualized combat, men imitate the animals.

In all sports, like football, where the aggressive instinct is allowed to function, all the needs of this instinctual drive are fulfilled, without murder. Someone wins; someone loses. The fight ends on a signal. The victor feels complete satisfaction.

The loser is allowed to live—and can vow to fight better on another day.

But all of us cannot be professional football players. Few people, in fact, can release their aggressive drive in the football stadium by actual participation. Most of us are spectators in the stands.

The spectators, however, share in the excitement and the release of aggression. When a bone-rattling tackle is made, a stadium-wide wince bounces from one side to the other. When one's home team scores, spectators and players alike jump up, shake their arms and cheer. In short, the crowd roars, the crowd groans and the crowd leaves after the game exhausted and happy—or exhausted and sad but oddly happy in the knowledge that they did their best and the better team won.

Proof of the fact that the on-lookers share in the expression of each person's aggressive instinct is not hard to find. The cries of "Kill the umpire" and "Booooo" are heard throughout the land. "Hold that line" and "We want a touchdown," overlap with the baseball cries and mingle with the hysterical screams and shouts coming from the stands at a basketball game. Hockey fans, as is well-known, are in a continual state of uproar and no distinguishable cries can be separated from the prolonged (game-long) roar that blankets the chill air around the ice-coated arena.

There are other ways in which man satisfies his aggressive instincts without murdering his fellows. Many of these are actually displacement activities, common to animals that are inhibited against murder. The pecking order of hens is aped in man by the old story of the tired executive who cannot strike his boss but manages to go home and get into a fight with his wife who in turn finds fault with young son—who in turn kicks the dog. The dog yelps and wonders what is going on but soon curls up at the youngster's feet again, sure that eventually a pat on the head will be coming along.

In extreme cases of displacement behavior, two grown-up men will shout at one another but instead of striking each other, will pound a desk or a table. This displacement behavior was never more amusingly seen than when Premier Khrushchev of the Soviet Union stood at the United Nations making an ass of himself by banging on the desk with his shoe. The displacement activity worked, however, since this turned-aside aggression made Mr. Khrushchev feel better and perhaps avoided a "showdown" fight.

Social workers argue that if gangs like the Egyptian Kings and the Jesters could find stimulation and a release in aggression in sports or some constructive displacement activity, murder and violence would be avoided. These efforts have been made many times. Sometimes they are successful and sometimes they are not. As yet no one knows exactly why they work in some cases, but fail to stop murder in others.

The Roar of the Crowd

There is something stimulating in becoming part of a crowd or group with a single purpose. When we go to a football game we begin to merge with the crowd the minute we leave our cars. Private cares, quarrels and concerns evaporate from our minds. In short, we lose our identity for awhile as individuals and focus on a simple common purpose of the crowd. The purpose, of course, at the football game is to defeat an enemy in the ritual fight. And it is both comforting and stimulating to look around at the sea of faces on "our side" and know that all of those people are allies in the cause.

The band plays a stirring rhythm. Cheerleaders organize and lead the rhythmic noises the crowd makes. The uniformed players run onto the field.

And here, in this peaceful scene—or controlled, if not peaceful—are the elements that can lead men to murder: a crowd, a cause and a leader. Our feeling of stimulation gained from forgetting personal problems on entering the stadium is increased by all the psychological tricks we can devise: the identical uniforms of the players; the rhythmic chants; the martial music; the sense of unity and purpose—a purpose simple enough for all to grasp and one that appeals to our deepest instinct of group preservation: the defeat of an enemy who threatens us.

During the early summer of 1968, there was a great deal of this sort of activity going on. The presidential campaign was warming up. The civil rights leaders were planning and executing marches and demonstrations. The violence preaching leaders were organizing their tactics and making threats. At no time in history has there been such a great number of opportunities to study crowd behavior. In each case there are the three necessary elements: a crowd, a leader and a cause.

Members of the political establishment usually like to point to the campaign hysteria as a good American institution but this year the same psychology is being used for purposes of violence and disruption. The psychology will work for all groups. As individual members of the groups care less about their own aims, as they submerge their identities in the crowd of their belief, they will be increasingly responsive to the phrases of the politicians or demonstration leaders. These phrases, come to think of it, begin to sound oddly alike as the tempo increases and rational thought takes a back seat.

The appeal in speeches comes from pointing out a real or imagined enemy against which the group can exert its force. When politicians begin to use the timeless and general phrases to excite enthusiasm, you can be sure the uproar is in full swing. Issues hinted at in the early days of the campaign; issues analyzed by journalists; issues that are supposed to define the process of selecting a president all disappear from the speeches. Instead, the speechmaker, whether political or riot-inciting, uses the old familiar phrases that have haunted men since wars began:

> "Fighting the forces of evil"
> "Defense of all we hold dear"
> "Fight to be free"
> "Preserve our freedom."

Clichés? Yes. But they work—as politicians have known for centuries. The same phrases translated into appropriate Russian, echo across Red Square with monstrous regularity. In France, in China, in Africa, in Israel, in Egypt and Jordan. It's getting to be quite a list, isn't it?

For many years the world has lived under the threat of mankind blowing up mankind with nuclear weapons. And nuclear scientists have been among the most concerned people involved—principally because they are involved in the creation, testing and perfecting the weapons of world destruction. As a grim reminder of the situation, the periodic Bulletin of Atomic Scientists has carried a feature, a clock with the hands set at twelve minutes to midnight. It represents, to the scientists, how close or far away they believe ultimate destruction may be. Midnight symbolizes Doomsday. The first issue of 1968 showed the clock with the hands moved five minutes closer to midnight. The reason given for the upsetting change was not direct nuclear threat. It was the sudden and alarming increase in violence and fist-shaking nationalism that has suddenly infected the world. In country after country reports have come that, for some reason, the nation's leaders are no longer respected, that leaders can no longer control what they have roused. Violence has spread like a chain reaction among crowds all over the world. This violence, coupled with intense nationalism, could, in the minds of the atomic scientists, lead to a war or wars that would force the nuclear powers into a final showdown.

CHAPTER X

A Grapple with The Nitty Gritty

THERE IS an ugly rumor afoot that mankind is insane.

This thought has occurred to many people in years past and they have put it into words on more than one occasion. People laughed. They thought the idea delightful. So everybody's got a few buttons missing. So what?

Evidence to support the ugly rumor has begun to pile up at a great rate in the past few years. The evidence does not refer to an increase in the admission of patients to mental hospitals. Nor does it refer to the great expansion in the nation's mental health program. Not even to the headlined increase in crime throughout the country.

It points to the possible fact that mankind is insane.

There are three main areas of man's activities that have led experts in all three fields to entertain the thought that the human species is about to commit suicide. Now the suicide of an individual is generally admitted to be caused by a major disorder. Whatever word is used, the inference is the same: disordered, highly disturbed, psychotic, nuts. And if an entire species commits suicide, the remaining species (if any) would be justified in raising a hoof, paw, or wing and make circles in the air at one side of their collective heads.

The three main areas of human activity that offer evidence of mankind's insanity are:

1) Environment Destruction
2) Breeding Rate
3) The Violent Destruction of Our Own Species

Any one of the three activities could do the job and the groundwork has already been laid in all three areas to do just what we say we do not want to do: end human life on earth—perhaps *all* life on earth.

Environment Destruction

Chapter VIII introduced the thought of MEVN, Man's Eye View of Nature. In that chapter, MEVN referred to our using animals and all natural resources as we damn well pleased. The Judeo-Christian ideas justified it. There are other forces at work, too, that help man destroy the earth. Several primary ones are ignorance, science and technology, greed, and desire for the "good life."

All of these forces act both separately and together. In some situations, a single one of them can be seen working, but for the most part they are interlocked. For purposes of analysis, however, let's look at them one by one.

Ignorance: Ecology is the science of environments and the interaction of all its elements, plant and animal. Ecologists today are deeply concerned about men disrupting environments without knowing the consequences of their acts. All too frequently, some specialist or interested party will alter a particular environment and then watch with mounting uneasiness the consequences of what he did.

There are many examples of this. One that comes to mind took place many years ago in California. In the mountains of the coastal range, there used to be many mountain lions. And these, as we all know, are fearsome savage beasts who leap on unsuspecting citizens all the time. What started the chain of events, however, was not the lions killing people (actually no people were killed, as you know, but the fear remains) but the lions killing the deer. Now those deer were the lion's natural prey. They were breakfast, lunch, and dinner. But when motorists came across the torn carcasses of the deer, they were outraged. Women were particularly incensed because the lions killed does and fawns as well as—or sometimes in preference to—the antlered bucks. The good ladies raised a hue and cry at this example of evil, bestial behavior. So the call went out: "Kill the lions." Accordingly the lions were killed. The deer multiplied. They overgrazed the mountain sides, browsing happily on the lower foliage of bushes that held the soil in place. With the overgrazing came the rains. The soil on the stripped sides of the mountains gave way and what was a naturally balanced environment of lions, deer, trees, shrubs, topsoil and all other forms of life it housed, became instead, a desert on the mountain slopes.

Ignorance of the consequences of tinkering with the environment is not limited to sentimental ladies. Scientists, engineers and government officials make their important contributions. Consider the apparently desirable effort to "reclaim" land where there is little rainfall by irrigating it. This, it seems, will be a "good thing." But history in the Near East and elsewhere has shown that irrigation of land can eventually lead to its total agricultural destruction through what is called salinization.

Irrigated areas are supplied with fresh water from some source as near to the fields as possible. It may be a river or, in modern times, the source may be a man-made dam that impounds a stream. When the water reaches the dry land it soaks in. More water is pumped in until the water table beneath that land rises to the tillable layer of earth. Then any more water pumped in stays on or near the surface and supplies the plants grown there. But the sun evaporates the water and this evaporation draws water up from deep in the earth. That water has dissolved a great many salts that were in the earth. The slightly saline water reaches the surface and evaporates, leaving the salt on the surface. Over the years, this increase in the salt on the surface makes the area permanently unsuitable for growing crops. But we go on irrigating land—to feed a growing number of people on the earth.

Scientists have begun tinkering with the weather, too. In 1967, $150,000,000 was asked of Congress for research in weather control. What would the effects be if we did control the weather? We do not know. Some years ago, this question of weather control was put to a meteorologist who was enthusiastically plying his trade of weather plotting and forecasting. When asked what he thought the consequences might be and whether man should try to do this, he replied with a shrug, "If he can, he will."

Science and Technology: Like the navigator who got lost

in the airplane while fiddling with the radio compass, many scientists are so "locked in" on their research project that they lose the wider view of what they are doing. They do not, in short, look out the window and try to recognize the landscape. Engineers working on advanced technology problems have a similarly narrow view. They *have* to narrow their view for the simple reason that they have so much to learn and retain to stay on top of the problem that they have no time left for consideration of other things.

The unsettling part of all this is that with the aid of the very machines and theories they have invented or discovered, scientists and technologists multiply their attack on the environment a hundred or a thousand times.

Not long ago a new detergent was perfected by some chemists working for a large business corporation. It did everything they wanted it to do. Cleaned clothes whiter than snow, or snow-white, or what have you. It had only one drawback, but not one that bothered the business executives or chemists a bit. The detergent would not "break down" in the soil after being released into it. The detergent began to pollute wells. Not until a great many complaints came in did the company do anything about it.

This detergent came to the attention of the public but most such chemicals do not. They are used and thrown down the drain. Which means eventually down the river; which means into the oceans. At the present time we are discharging 500,000 different kinds of waste products into the ocean.

To most people, jet air travel is nice. The development of jet aircraft, as speedy and luxurious as we have, is considered a marvel of technology. But among the end products of the burning jet fuel is carbon dioxide. A big four-engine jet plane flying through the atmosphere spews fifteen tons of carbon dioxide into the sky every hour. When you think of the number of planes that fly to New York City every day (nearly 1500), and the number of times these aircraft are "stacked" in a waiting pattern to be cleared for landing, there is little wonder that the atmosphere of New York City is not something any person likes to inhale.

The wonders of the nuclear age have been drummed into an entire generation of people. Bombs aside, we believe that the "peaceful" use of atomic energy will be a great boon to all. For one thing, it is argued by scientists working on such projects, this will mean that the smoke-producing, airpolluting fossil fuels (oil, natural gas, and coal) will no longer do their damage to the environment. But the present reactors being built to supply power for the cities and towns of several regions are producing a radioactive and life-killing "waste product" composed of Strontium-90 and Cesium-137. These wastes have to be put somewhere for 1000 years before they lose their harmful radioactivity. They are being sealed in stored containers—and it has been reported that the containers are leaking.

So ignorance, day by day, plays its part in making the earth uninhabitable.

Greed: No sooner does a scientist or engineer develop a new product than the marketing manager is called in to see how soon and how much money can be made from the discovery. The effect that the product will have on the environment is the furthest thing from their minds as they discuss the problem. If it is in the food or drug areas, of course the new product must pass government inspection. But if the discovery is radically new, even the scientists working for the government trying to protect both the people and the environment cannot foretell what its effect will be. The new product is hailed as an example of further scientific progress and packaged and sold as rapidly as possible.

While the impact of a new product on the earth's environment cannot be foretold, the effects of mining, timbering, and overplanting don't need to be foretold. They're here right now for all to see.

Few people have heard of Ducktown, Tennessee. But at one time it was better known than any other city in the state. It was the location of a large deposit of copper discovered around 1840. Into the wilderness, as it then was, streamed the miners, the builders, the speculators. Ore was dug from the ground and roasted using hardwood and charcoal cut from the surrounding forests. Gradually the forests were thinned and decreased and the acres of stripped ground increased. The ore had a good deal of sulfur in it and this was the impurity that was taken out by the roasting process. In the operation, as the wood fires burned and the haze settled over the forest, the sulfur combined with oxygen to produce sulfur dioxide. This in turn stayed in the air. Some of it dissolved in the falling rain and the condensed moisture on the ground, on the receding trees and other plant growth. The plant life withered and died. Year after year the ground absorbed the acid resulting from the combination of water and the sulfur dioxide. By the time the copper in the region had been exhausted, no single plant could grow in an area of nearly one hundred square miles. Men had created a desert in the midst of some of the most fertile, heavily treed land in the country.

The twentieth century came and in the 1930's the Federal Government made an attempt to reclaim the man-made desert. No known grass in the country would grow in that desert so the search widened and grasses from all over the world were tried. A South African grass appeared to be able to hold its own and it was planted in great quantities. To replace the cut timber, nearly two and a half million trees were planted. They died. Today, over a hundred years after its creation, that man-made desert remains a place where no life grows, where no bird sings.

You would think that in 100 years we would have learned something from Ducktown, Tennessee. But strip mining goes on at a faster pace now with bigger shovels and trucks and the same disregard of the insane destruction of more landscape. It is just possible that some truck driver jolts his way along a road in the desolate hills carrying coal or ore humming the MEVN song: *This Land Is My Land.* In fact it is entirely possible that he bursts into song when he reaches the line "This land was made for you and me."

Desire for the "Good Life:" It is hard to see how a desire for what we have been taught are the "good things in life" can help wreck the environment. At least at first glance. In the United States and, increasingly, in other lands, the comforts of twentieth century civilization are being taken for granted. New cars—every year or two, new air conditioners, refrigerators, cigarettes, cosmetics. Coupled with our crazy breeding habits, however, it becomes clear that to supply all these terribly essential things something has to produce them. The something is in most cases such gigantic corporations as: General Motors, General Electric, General Foods, General Dynamics. Generally speaking then, we have a culture that demands comforts and conveniences and the giant plants and enterprises to supply them. The wood, the iron, the copper, the fuel, the food all are being popped out of the environment faster and faster and, of course, the waste products are popped back in.

In his book, *The New Industrial State,* John Kenneth Galbraith makes the point that one of the most important commandments within giant corporations is: Thou Shalt Show the Greatest Possible Annual Growth. Growth means sales, so they sell their products. To more and more people, faster and faster. Eternal, unlimited, infinite growth is what is demanded whatever it does to resources, to the land, to the planet itself. In nature there are similar runaway growths, a kind of insanity of limitless production. Like cancer.

A fictional observer of the human scene, perhaps from another, wiser, culture on another planet would watch this burrowing into the ground for minerals, this frantic production of goods that are used briefly and then thrown away, this fouling of the atmosphere and the laying waste of the land, and conclude that indeed *homo sapiens,* man the wise, had lost his marbles.

Breeding Rate

In all species of animals that men have studied—with the

exception of man—there is some mechanism that prevents population explosions. When the population in an environment rises above a critical level the mechanism is triggered and the animals, depending on their species, either stop caring for their young (as in rats) or die from stress symptoms due to overcrowding. Deer and rabbits are subject to this kind of control. (In the example of the deer overgrazing on the California mountainside mentioned earlier, the deer population eventually regulated itself but not until local damage to the undergrowth had occurred.)

With men, the situation seems to be almost exactly reversed. Where overcrowding does *not* occur, populations are fairly stable. Where it *does* occur, the rate of reproduction soars. Among the poor in the crowded cities of Latin America, China and India the annual population rise is about three per cent. In relatively affluent and uncrowded Europe and America—and even in crowded but modern Japan—the rate is about 1.7%.

Two hundred years ago, India had a population of sixty million people. Today it is over 500 million. By 2000 A.D. it will be close to one billion. Efforts have been made to halt India's population. When it was evident that this could not be done, the concerned experts hoped they could at least slow its growth. This, too, failed.

No other problem facing mankind is as obvious as the rate of population growth—and the term "population explosion" has been used so much that it doesn't bother people to hear it any longer. It is accepted as a fact of life. But consider this. It took one million years for man's population to reach the estimated 3.25 billion we have now. At the present rate of growth, it takes only about thirty-five years to double that number.

In countries where, in years past, sickness, plague, and starvation killed many of a family's children before they reached adulthood, it was customary to produce as many children as possible to insure the continuance of the family. But modern medicine and food distribution (however faulty) has cut the death rate drastically, and human life has been prolonged far beyond what it was a century ago—still these families produce children for the old, no longer rational reason that they *must* to insure the family's continuing.

One author has pointed up the problem in unmistakable terms. Within the lifetime of the present teenage generation the population of the world will have reached a point where it can no longer be fed. For even if we did not destroy the land, if we put it under the most advanced form of cultivation, taking the greatest care to preserve it, there simply is not enough acreage to raise enough food to feed the people that will be walking around. We will have to overrun the earth in a very literal manner—with billions of our feet.

The senseless increase in population coupled with the continued destruction of our soil and our race to exhaust all other natural resources cannot be regarded as sane actions. These two factors alone would lead most people to conclude that man is not quite right in the head.

The Violent Destruction of Our Own Species

Nearly all people concerned with the violent destruction of

men by men have looked long and hard at man's aggressive instinct. This, they believed, was the cause of murder and of lynching and the root cause of war. But aggression has been shown to be a species preserving instinct, not a destructive one. And a logical mind might think "Both these views of aggression cannot be true." Perhaps the time has come to look elsewhere for the source of destruction.

All people, everywhere, belong to a larger group they call their society. At times, the single person acts as a single person. He asserts himself, he plans for what he wants without too much concern for the larger group. But all the while he knows and accepts his part in the group. In the family, for instance, there is a constant tension between what each individual wants and what the family requires. This is the normal state of affairs. As part of a nation, a religion, a political party or any other organization, individuals also subordinate their individual, self-assertive natures at times and find satisfaction in doing what the group requires. This giving up of one's individual aims can often be quite pleasurable. It is called self-transcendance.

Remember the roaring crowd at the football game? In it, you gladly left your personal cares and aims behind when you entered the stadium. There was an exhilaration in being a member of the group; there was a self-forgetfulness and a greater fulfillment of yourself at the same time. You may actually have done things at the ball game that you do not normally do. Slap a stranger on the back in your excitement. Talk enthusiastically with someone you have never met, about the game and the common goal. Later, by yourself, you may even have been a little shocked at your behavior. But it seemed justified at the time. It was in a good cause.

Groups that gather at football games soon dissolve. Of course the memory of the experience lingers. And if the game involved your school or college, your loyalty to the idea of your school or college makes you think of yourself as a permanent member of a group. Various psychological devices are employed to keep you a member of the group and they are harmless enough (school colors, song and yearbook). The point here is that you do not have to be in the physical presence of all the group members to share their beliefs, to respond to the self-transcending exhilaration of being a group member. You can enjoy the feeling even when you are alone.

Experienced political leaders have the talent or gift of knowing how to appeal to large masses of people, to get them to relinquish their individual goals and become, quite happily, a part of a group. The underlying trick in their talent is simple: speak of a simple theme that even the least intelligent person can understand; appeal to a deep-seated, universal emotion. Example: Our goal is progress (simple theme) but they are trying to stop us (rousing fear by pointing to an invisible enemy).

Another example: Keep the faith, Baby. The simple theme is faith (which faith or what the faith really means depends on who says it and who is listening). The emotion-rousing part is equally simple here: keep. The idea here is that someone is trying to take your faith away from you. You are supposed to resist them.

There are countless other possible examples, of course. But all of them make their appeal to our emotions, not our reason. All of them require self-transcendance, commitment of our emotions to the simple theme. Once this has been accomplished, the person has become in every sense of the phrase a "true-believer." The darling of leaders everywhere.

Some astonishing things can happen to very intelligent people when this condition is reached. They no longer listen to rational argument. They are skillful at answering opposing arguments or rejecting evidence that would upset their belief system. A good example of this comes from fairly recent history. During the Stalinist era in Communist Russia, a great many people were murdered. Many of these starved to death over vast areas of the land. Since Communism was supposed to be ushering in the new Utopia, the dreamed-about heaven on earth, this seemed to outsiders to be a strange way of doing the job. But it did not bother the true believer at all. Very intelligent men from Europe and the United States at that time believed in Communism. They visited Russia during those sad times and saw the starving people. There, you might say, was evidence that ought to change the beliefs of anyone who saw it. Not so. These intelligent people used their brain (the distinguishing feature between man and non-man) to justify their belief system.

How in the world could they do that?

Easily. The starving people represented the inherited problem of the old Czarist order. But under Communism, tomorrow would be brighter. In other words use the skillful brain, use reason, to justify whatever belief system you may have embraced.

You might be getting the feeling that this sounds pretty crazy.

But we all do it. Our belief systems are not embraced because of any intelligent conclusion. They are embraced because of a powerful appeal to simple, universal, timeless emotions. And our large forebrains do not control these emotions. The key word here is *control*.

We live, in our day to day lives, on a kind of tightrope. One end is fastened to our emotional self; the other to our mental or intelligent self. We are balanced on the tightrope constantly and there is no net underneath.

When intelligent people become upset they have just missed their footing on that tightrope. And we all do that from time to time. Of course in most cases, involving personal matters the results are not too serious. But they are very good examples of the tightrope theory. On one occasion I had lunch with an internationally known scientist. We had an amiable time and when we went to the cashier's cage, he asked the little old lady behind the cage to change a ten dollar bill. He asked politely enough. But she, without explaining that she had a limited amount of change at the moment, said one word: no.

He went off like a rocket. He, a full professor in one of the greatest technical universities in the world and she, a lady who probably had not finished high school, were in a spit-showering rage within fifteen seconds.

It would seem evident that our large forebrains do not control our emotions. The very best they can do is keep them in check part of the time. You can even argue that many times, more times than we like to admit, our emotions control our intellects. And all attempts to use reason to control the emotions when a belief system is threatened—or is *thought* to be threatened—have proven useless. You might as well try to argue with a madman.

From prehistoric times men have subscribed to belief systems of one kind or another. And for about that length of time men have been appealing to man's reason to stop wars. This has taken the form of persuasive argument down the centuries. Lately it has taken the form of a scientific approach. The catch is that the scientific efforts have been directed at man's instinctual aggressive drive, not his capability for self-transcendance, his ability to embrace a belief system and die for a cause—or kill for it.

But, someone may ask, is not our ability to transcend ourselves responsible for all the good men do? All the great works of art and religion and human selflessness? All that we regard as the highest achievement of mankind? All that separates him from the "animals?"

Yes it is but there are two sides to the coin. The dark thread of killing his fellowman (uninhibited in men's evolution) is woven with the white thread of selfless, humane acts. And the trouble is everyone points proudly at the white thread, ignores the black one and blames man's "animal inheritance" for the murder that continues.

There would seem to be something wrong with man's head. He deludes himself easily. He can read a story of a made-up person, like Little Nell, and cry his eyes out because of black symbols printed on a white page. He can see enemies stretching into infinity who are trying to upset his belief system—whether it is Communism or free-enterprise or orthodox religion or orthodox politics (*his* orthodox religion or *his* orthodox politics).

The evolution of man's large forebrain is one of the most astonishing mutations that nature has produced. Compared with the time required for the evolution of wings from legs, of feathers from scales it happened in seconds. And unlike most evolutionary processes, the large forebrain did not replace the reptilian and mammalian brains we had originally. The large forebrain grew right on top of the lower brains. Packed right in there and connected to them.

The forebrain or neocortex, thinks. It thinks in words that we can understand—the words that are the symbols that the neocortex conceived. It allows us to carry on the unceasing dialogue with ourselves that may be called the conscious self. Unhappily, the lower brains don't know any words. This makes it difficult for the neocortex to communicate with the lower brains and you might say "So what. They haven't got anything to teach us anyway." They're not trying to teach us anything. They just are there—controlling our emotions. When we sweat; when adrenal is discharged into our bodies; when fear or anger are roused—those lower centers are getting the message across. And the real bright neocortex can't tell them to slow down very effectively.

All belief systems appeal to the true believers on the basis of deep emotional response, response that comes from the less highly developed lower brains. Politicians, rabble rousers, evangelists all understand this whether they know the physiology or not. They lull the forebrain to sleep by giving it no food for thought (the simple theme) and make their appeal to the emotions—to the essentially non-verbal emotion-controlling centers of the lower brain. Faith is the watchword. Not reason.

It is safe to say that no widespread belief-system can exist among men in their present state of evolution without appealing to the no-thought part of their brains.

Man's brain is split. Man is schizoid. Delusionary. Insane.

There is, of course, connective tissue between the forebrain, the neocortex and the lower brains, the limbic node as it is called. Messages get through but it all too frequently is a one-way street. Our emotions color and control our thoughts much more frequently than our thoughts control our emotions. Of course, thought controls emotions to some extent. But when we have willingly stopped thinking (i.e. joined a belief system) then the big trouble starts.

Let's consider again man's highest achievements coming from the quality of self-transcendance that man shows. Take the case of Little Nell that made the reader cry. Now Little Nell is not exactly man's highest achievement but the process that created Little Nell is a workable example.

The creative process that produced Little Nell (or Beethoven's Ninth Symphony, or Peanuts and all the others) is not clearly understood. But in this process there is excellent communication between neocortex and the emotion-controlling limbic node within the artist. Consider what he is doing. He conceives of a character (how he does not quite know) and using the symbol cluttered neocortex refers the problem to the emotion-rousing nonverbal limbic node. By monitoring what comes back through the connective tissue with his neo-cortex, he selects the emotions, weaves them into a more or less sophisticated consciousness, translates them into abstract characters and puts them on a piece of paper. You read the story or hear the music and cry or laugh or do whatever the artist had in mind for you to do. He deludes you but manages himself to remain undeluded. He has established, at least dur-ing his creation of the work, a mutually beneficial communi-cation between his verbalizing neocortex and his grunt, groan, gnash, sweat, spring, sleep non-verbal limbic node.

Of course, when the creating is over, the artist acts like any other mortal idiot.

So the idea that our large forebrains and our self-transcending ability are unalloyed benefits to the species has two flaws in it. The first is the example above. High achievements in esthetics represent harmonious communication between the neocortex and the limbic node—the situation sought for—not a denial of the dual nature of our brains. The second flaw is statistical. The high achievements of mankind are produced by a fraction of a fraction of one per cent of mankind. Their beneficial self-transcendance is so rare as to be an abnormality. Destructive self-transcendance is universal.

Whither

So man, with his early animal inheritance has the instincts that can preserve him. He is territorial and he is aggressive. Both of these instincts, as we have seen, in other animals serve a useful purpose. They can, and sometimes do, in man. But they can also be put at the service of his split mind.

The aggressive instinct leads to fights. By and large, the fights are not too murderous when the aggression is roused in a single individual by a single individual. There may be a fist fight between men or much hair-pulling and scratching between women. The damage is slight and the urge to fight soon satisfied. But this same instinct of aggression when put in the service of a self-transcending belief system can allow men to drop bombs, to press buttons releasing rockets, to kill millions of men in gas chambers—and sleep comfortably at night with no hint of guilt, no sense of being nuts. The believer believes he is fighting for legitimate reasons and he himself is willing to die for them. Aggression here is at the service of his delusion.

It is interesting to watch the delusion work on the territorial instinct. Communists see their "territory" as being a conceived belief system—not primarily geography. Everyone must become a true believer within the territorial boundaries of the belief system. Likewise, all good American sales managers believe that the world is their territory, too—only they call it "market." They believe in the free-enterprise system and they, like the Communists, will cheerfully kill or have killed, all those who threaten their imagined territory.

Looking back to our destruction of the natural environment, to our belief system of science-technology, to our everexpanding markets, we can see the delusion at work. The population explosion can be traced here, too. Part of it is based on a belief system centuries old (and valid then, but no longer) that for survival, man must produce many children; yet the old belief system prevails.

If mankind is insane, what can mankind do about it? The question is difficult. Perhaps one way to go about answering it is to suggest that appeals to reason have been made in the past to keep men from killing each other and while they have worked some places and for some short periods of time they evidently do not produce the solution.

Can a madman cure himself? That's the real question. Arthur Koestler, the science-philosopher, has made the point that madmen are not mad all the time. There are periods of sanity when reason can be put to work. He envisions developments in the biochemical field of research that may heal the split mind of man. If we can produce, as he says, a dynamic equilibrium between the two split portions of the brain there is hope that the endless killing of men may be brought under control.

It would be nice to find a cheerful note on which to end this book. About the best that can be done, though, is to point out that until anyone is aware of a problem, the hope of solving it is zero. But being aware of the problem—its nature and size— is at least a first step.